SCIENCE AND POLITICS
IN THE
ANCIENT WORLD

by the same author

PRIMUM GRAIUS HOMO
Cambridge University Press

SCIENCE IN ANTIQUITY
Home University Library

THE CIVILIZATION
OF GREECE AND ROME
Gollancz

SCIENCE AND POLITICS
IN THE
ANCIENT WORLD

BY

BENJAMIN FARRINGTON

*Professor of Classics, University College
Swansea*

LONDON
GEORGE ALLEN & UNWIN LTD

FIRST PUBLISHED IN 1939

PRINTED IN GREAT BRITAIN
in 12-Point Bembo Type
BY UNWIN BROTHERS LIMITED
WOKING

Οὐ κόμπου οὐδὲ φωνῆς ἐργαστικοὺς οὐδὲ τὴν περιμάχητον παρὰ τοῖς πολλοῖς παιδείαν ἐνδεικνυμένους φυσιολογία παρασκευάζει, ἀλλὰ σοβαροὺς καὶ αὐτάρκεις καὶ ἐπὶ τοῖς ἰδίοις ἀγαθοῖς, οὐκ ἐπὶ τοῖς τῶν πραγμάτων μέγα φρονοῦντας.

EPICURUS

The knowledge of natural law does not produce men given to idle boasting or prone to display the culture for which the many strive, but men of a haughty independence of mind who pride themselves on the goods proper to man, not to his circumstances.

Acknowledgments

I wish to thank the following: Dr. Cyril Bailey for permission to quote from his translation of Epicurus; A. and C. Black, Ltd., for permission to quote from Thomas Whittaker's *Priests, Philosophers and Prophets*; G. Bell and Sons, Ltd., for permission to quote from Munro's translation of Lucretius; Mr. W. H. S. Jones for permission to quote from his version of the Hippocratic writings (Loeb Library, Heinemann); the Jowett Trustees for permission to quote from Jowett's translation of *The Republic of Plato* (O.U.P.); John Murray for permission to quote from A. W. Benn's *The Greek Philosophers*; and Professor George Thomson for permission to quote from his version of the *Prometheus* of Aeschylus.

Contents

List of Chief Figures from Antiquity

PAGAN ERA

THALES, *fl. c.* 585
ANAXIMANDER, *c.* 610–546
ANAXIMENES, *fl. c.* 546
PYTHAGORAS, *c.* 572–500
XENOPHANES, *c.* 580–480
THEOGNIS, *fl. c.* 520
AESCHYLUS, 525–456
PINDAR, 522–448
HERACLITUS, *fl. c.* 504
PARMENIDES, *fl. c.* 504
ANAXAGORAS, 500–428
PROTAGORAS, 480–411
EURIPIDES, 480–406
EMPEDOCLES, *fl. c.* 445
DEMOCRITUS, *fl. c.* 420

HIPPOCRATES OF COS, *c.* 460–380
SOCRATES, 469–399
ISOCRATES, 436–338
PLATO, 427–347
ARISTOTLE, 384–322
EPICURUS, 341–270
ZENO, 336–264
ARCHIMEDES, 287–212
POLYBIUS, 198–117
PANAETIUS, *c.* 180–110
VARRO, 116–27
LUCRETIUS, 98–55
CICERO, 106–43
DIODORUS SICULUS, *c.* 90–30

CHRISTIAN ERA

MANILIUS, *fl. c.* 12
SENECA, *died* 65
PLUTARCH, *died* 125
TERTULLIAN, *died* 220

ORIGEN, 185–254
ST. AUGUSTINE, 354–430
PRUDENTIUS, *fl.* 400
COSMAS INDICOPLEUSTES, *fl.* 540

CHAPTER ONE

INTRODUCTORY

A MODERN ILLUSTRATION

Haeckel, by stressing the application to Man of Darwin's theory of the Origin of Species, finds that he has transformed himself from a pure scientist to a politician.

This is a book about the obstacles to the spread of a scientific outlook in the ancient world. Of these obstacles the chief is generally characterized as Popular Superstition. The purpose of this study is to raise the question how far popular superstition means superstition originated by the people or imposed upon the people. Plutarch, in his brilliant essay On Superstitition, says of the victims of this disease that "they despise Philosophers and Grave Personages of State and Government, who do teach and show that the Majesty of God is accompanied with bounty, magnanimity, love and careful regard of our good." [1] But we shall find much evidence to show that philosophers and grave personages of State and Government inculcated also less comfortable doctrines of acknowledged falsity. Ancient writers will inform us of the nature of these doctrines and the motive for their dissemination. Their testimony will help us to distinguish between the two sources of ancient superstition, popular ignorance and deliberate deceit. To the writer it seems that the keeping of this elementary distinction results in a shifting of the perspective in which the history of science in antiquity is seen and in the clarifying of several issues that were previously obscure. Above all, it throws light on the history of Epicureanism, and on the strange figure of the Latin poet Lucretius, in whose work the war against superstition reached its highest expression in the ancient world.

In the later chapters of this book we shall be concerned to trace the interactions between Natural Philosophy and Political Philosophy in the world of Classical Antiquity. In our view the development of Natural Philosophy was violently interfered with by considerations that arose in a field extraneous to it, namely politics. The invasion of the domain of Natural Philosophy by political ideas is most evident in Plato. The last determined endeavour to rescue Natural Philosophy from politics was made by Lucretius. Our enquiry, therefore, though it will start before Plato and continue after Lucretius, will centre mainly round these two great figures. But since it may not be immediately apparent that Natural Philosophy and Politics can and do interact, it may be well to give first an example from modern times of such interaction.

Among the advocates of the biological theory of evolution which produced such a ferment, not only in scientific circles but in society in general, in the closing decades of the nineteenth century one of the most prominent and most zealous was Ernst Haeckel. Round his head broke the most violent storms of controversy. Haeckel was a member of the upper classes with no particular interest in social problems. Only experience revealed to him, and the revelation puzzled him somewhat to his dying day, that an uncompromising public championship of his scientific views was a form of political action which roused the sharpest controversy and made him a hero to one political party and an object of suspicion to another.

Darwin, when he published his *Origin of Species* in 1859,

soft-pedalled its application to the origin of man. He provided his book with a theistic conclusion, and merely
suggested *en passant*, as among the probable results of his
theory of Natural Selection, that "light will be thrown on
the origin and history of humanity." His German translator,
Bronn, whose version appeared in 1860, still more timid
than Darwin, thought it better not to render the passage
at all. He simply omitted the dangerous sentence. But at
a scientific congress at Stettin in 1863 Haeckel, who was
the first speaker, vigorously underlined the implications for
the natural history of man that must logically be developed
from Darwin's theory. He had the general approval of his
colleagues, Virchow among them. But Virchow had a sense
for the social implications of science that Haeckel in his
innocence did not yet possess. At a later stage of the same
congress he proceeded to limit the field of action of science
in a sense the full significance of which did not become
clear for many years. It was the business of the scientist,
said Virchow, to establish facts, but not to go on to philo-
sophize about them. In the domain of fact science is supreme.
If it be established as a fact that man is descended from the
ape, no tradition in the world will be able to suppress the
fact. And the supremacy of science in the domain of fact
must be respected even beyond its frontiers. Church and
State must both bow to science in the realm of fact. "The
far-seeing Government and the open-minded Church will
always assimilate these advancing and developing ideas and
make them fruitful." But at the same time, said Virchow,
science must not seek to trespass beyond its frontiers. And
in the drawing of those mysterious frontiers Virchow showed
a wish to compromise with the claims of the far-seeing
Government and the open-minded Church which was later to
produce the sharpest divergence between him and Haeckel.

At the Stettin congress Virchow did not indicate the nature of the compromise he sought with Government. His concession was to the Church, and very curious was the line he drew between the spheres of Science and the Church. Consciousness, said Virchow, and above all those facts of consciousness that dominate our whole higher life, can never be the concern of science. "That is, I think," he said, "the point where science makes its compromise with the Churches, recognizing that this is a province that each can survey as he will, either putting his own interpretation on it or accepting the traditional ideas; and it must be sacred to others."

Virchow's position was anything but completely clear, but enough of it was clear to be inacceptable to Haeckel. The scientist might gather facts but he must not draw conclusions, at least in the sphere of consciousness. To impose such a compromise on Haeckel would have been to forbid him to think. He was to be free to trace the evolution of the physical structure of living things from the moneron to man, but not free to associate therewith any conclusions on the evolution of the psychic activities that depend on the physical structure. Vesalius had already muttered under such restrictions three hundred years before. Haeckel continued to enquire, to speculate, and to publish. Virchow, now openly setting expediency above truth, moved into full opposition. At the congress of 1877, it was no longer with the open-minded Church (its power had declined in the meantime in Germany) that he sought to establish a compromise, but with the far-seeing Government, which for the moment was the more powerful of the two. This time, not the Deposit of the Faith, but Interests of State, were to define the limits of the scientist's activities. Darwinism was now opposed on the ground that the Social

16

Democrats had taken to it. Science was to be restricted because the people were becoming interested in its conclusions. Not truth but political expediency was to be the controlling factor in the growth of science.

Haeckel now felt himself crushed between the upper and the nether mill-stone. He had always dreaded the ignorance of the multitude; now he began to fear that his worst enemy was the alliance of the Church with the reactionary political party in Germany. Ignorance, he reflected, may be cured; the appeal to interest is always addressed to deaf ears. He had always concerned himself with publishing his conclusions to the educated non-specialist; now he would seek a wider public still. He would, if he could, enlighten the multitude. That way at least lay hope for the future of mankind. Haeckel had turned politician, but not by abandoning science; he had merely found that to be a consistent and courageous scientist was politics in the highest degree. With the composition of *The Riddle of the Universe* he addressed himself to the man in the street. The book, translated into fourteen languages, sold in its hundreds of thousands. The Jena professor, whose weak voice could hardly be heard in the lecture-room, had spoken to the world. His determination not only to enquire but to publish the results of his enquiries had transformed the very nature of his activities. His opinions ceased to be a matter of merely academic concern; they, and his right to express them, had become the symbol of a struggle of the people for emancipation. To his bewilderment, and possibly not altogether to his satisfaction, he was exalted to the rank of a prophet by the democracies of the world.

Such were the repercussions in Church and State of one man's advocacy of Darwinism at the end of the nineteenth century. If it was observed with alarm that he was being read by factory-workers and fishermen; if it was discovered in his own country that his works were "a fleck of shame on the escutcheon of Germany," "an attack on the foundations of religion and morality"; and in Glasgow that the impeccable author himself was "a man of notoriously licentious life," these phenomena have, as we shall see, their analogy in the history of science in the ancient world.[2]

[1] Plutarch's *de Superstitione*, chap. 6. Translation by Philemon Holland.
[2] The source for the account of Ernst Haeckel given in this chapter is *Haeckel, His Life and Work*; by Wilhelm Bölsche; translated by Joseph McCabe, Fisher Unwin, 1906.

CHAPTER TWO

A FIRST GLANCE AT OUR PROBLEM

FROM ANAXIMANDER TO COSMAS INDICOPLEUSTES

Anaximander, in the sixth century B.C., *teaches a theory of evolution based on observation. Cosmas, in the sixth century* A.D., *teaches a theory based on the Bible, that the universe is made on the model of the Tabernacle of Moses.*

Attention has often been directed to the "miraculous" rise of Greek science in sixth-century Ionia. Equally marvellous is the state of its decline in the sixth century of our own era after more than a thousand years of civilization. This being the phenomenon we hope to explain in some measure, it will be well to take a preliminary survey of it.

In the sixth century in Ionia, within the compass of the lifetime of two men, Thales and Anixamander, science achieved an astonishing development. It is a fact, which anyone can confirm who cares to take the trouble, that the kind of things that Anaximander was saying in his book *On Nature* were the same kind of things that an up-to-date writer puts forward to-day in a scientific handbook of the universe. Thus, Anaximander was already maintaining that the sun, moon, and stars, the earth, and the sea, were all made of one fundamental substance; that they came to occupy their present positions in the universe as a natural result of the motion with which the primary matter is endowed; that this motion tended to send the hot and fiery element to the outside of the universe, the cold and earthy to the centre, while water and mist lay between; that the earth was still undergoing a great process of change, owing to the fact that the encircling heat continually dried up the moisture from the sea and the surface of the earth, a process plainly proved by the observed phenomenon of raised beaches; that living things had been produced in the course of the natural process thus described and were under the necessity of adapting themselves to their environment or perishing; that "the first animals were produced in moisture, and were covered with a spiny tegument; in course of time they reached land; when the integument burst they quickly modified their mode of life"; and that "living creatures were born from the moist element when it had been evaporated by the sun; man, in the beginning resembled another animal, to wit, a fish." These were the kind of things Anaximander was writing. And he was further aware that he had arrived at these conclusions by looking at the universe about him and thinking about what he saw. He realized that the kind of things he was led by observation and reflection to believe about the universe constituted a new kind of knowledge not the same as that taught by poets and priests; but he thought that it could be trusted to make its way by itself with intelligent people and would be found useful to humanity. He himself began to apply his knowledge to the practical purpose of making a map of the known world.

People have been rightly astonished at the progress in science that was made in a generation in Ionia in the sixth century. But is it not even more astonishing that this promising beginning should in due time have completely failed? In the sixth century of our own era a writer called

Cosmas Indicopleustes, whose work has survived while only the smallest fragments of Anaximander's remain, set out to prove, in his *Christian Topography*, that the earth is a flat plain with high walls enclosing it on each of its four sides. He was led to this opinion not primarily by the examination of the world, but by a conviction that the world was made on the model of the tabernacle of Moses described in Holy Writ. With this supernatural guidance to aid him he knew that the sky was a semi-cylindrical lid which rested on the four walls and thus formed a cover for the plain. Other knowledge also he possessed. It had been a defect of Greek science that it had failed to develop a theory of energy, and much nonsense was believed and written by Greek philosophers on the question of the power that moved the heavenly bodies. But Cosmas had a solution for this problem also. According to him the motive power for the heavenly bodies was supplied by angels. It was angels who produced the phenomena of night and day, and other phenomena of the sort, by carrying the heavenly bodies round a high mountain that lay to the north of the plain. The defect of Greek science was thus made good. The foolish Greeks had hesitated on the threshold of a theory of energy; angels rushed in where fools had feared to tread. But the most significant thing of all is that Cosmas had parted with the idea that the universe is evidence of its own nature. This evidence is now to be derived not from study of nature but from study of a book; and this book is not believed because it is new, but because it is old; and not simply because it is old, but because it is supernatural. What causes had operated to produce the change from the world of Anaximander to the world of Cosmas Indicopleustes? This is the question with which we shall be concerned.

It may be objected that in contrasting Anaximander with

Cosmas we are contrasting one of the greatest of Greek thinkers with a Christian writer of no very great intellectual pretensions. But this objection is not valid, for the comparison is intended not between the individual thinkers, but between the two men as representative of their times, and both Anaximander and Cosmas are representative figures. If it had been a question of finding a better scientist than Cosmas in the sixth century of the Christian era, Joannes Philoponus, the distinguished commentator on Aristotle's *Physics*, who was converted from Neo-Platonism to Christianity about A.D. 520, would serve our turn. But Philoponus is not a typical figure. In so far as he was a scientist he represents the survival of a dying tradition. It was the opinion of Cosmas, namely, that in the Bible we have the key to the understanding of the nature of things, that was to be characteristic of the coming age.[1]

The problem, then, is to find an adequate cause for the decline of the scientific activity of the ancient world, the disappearance of the spirit of enquiry into the nature of things. Many answers have been suggested. Christianity has been blamed. But this is no answer to our problem; for, in so far as Christianity was incompatible with science, we have still to ask why the ancients abandoned their science for Christianity.

The inroads of the barbarian peoples on the frontiers of the Roman Empire are credited with the destruction of the tradition of civilization. But this raises the enormous question why the civilized portion of the world should have declined in power and the uncivilized portion increased, until the disproportion became so great that the barbarians overran the Empire. If science had been doing what science can do for mankind the Empire would never have fallen before the attack of the rude invaders.

Greek science, it has also been said, failed because the Romans could not assimilate it; when the Romans assumed the political mastery of the Greeks, the creative race was reduced to a subject position, and the Romans themselves could not take up the torch. But the racial incapacity of the Romans for science is a very doubtful argument, as doubtful as the supposed racial basis of the scientific achievement of the Greeks. There was no Greek race, and no Roman race. The Greek thinkers were, racially, a thoroughly mongrel lot. Then, as in the modern world, many of the most distinguished "European" scientists had a good porportion of oriental blood in their veins.[2] And if there was no Greek race with a special aptitude for science, there was no Roman race with a special inaptitude for it. The ancient Romans were as mixed a lot as the modern Italians; and if the modern Italians have contributed richly to science, while the ancient Romans contributed very little, the explanation does not lie in race.

External causes for the failure of ancient science proving insufficient, internal causes have been sought for. It has been said, with much justification, that the basis of Greek science was too narrow. Roughly it may be said that the Greeks, conspicuously successful in mathematics, failed in physics. They indulged in much physical speculation, but they did not establish a tradition of systematic experiment. Such experiments as they are known to have employed were rather in the nature of illustrations of speculative conclusions than part of a clearly apprehended technique of research. This explanation is good so far as it goes. But it still leaves the further question, *why* the development of Greek science should have been so lop-sided. To this again a partial answer has been given by those who point to the slave-basis of ancient society, and who see in the divorce of theory and practice that follows from the institution of slavery a reason for the development of the speculative and abstract side of science and the failure of its concrete applications.

To the present writer the line of explanation opened up by those who approach the problem of the failure of ancient science from the point of view of the social structure of ancient society seems the true one. The problem is complex, and in this essay only one aspect of it will be stressed. Many writers have shown a lively sympathy with the view that science is the creation of an élite and is endangered if it be entrusted to the ignorant mob. It is not so common to find any corresponding sense of the responsibility of governments for the existence of such ignorance; still less of the active part played by governments in the promotion of ignorance.

Salomon Reinach[3] accounts for the retrogressions towards animism and magic, whether in nineteenth-century France or fourth-century Greece, by "the admixture of minds emancipated, but few in number, with the ignorant and superstitious multitude." But though he does utter a reproach against the "cultivated rationalistic classes, which cared nothing for enlightening the poor folk," he shows no true sense of the issues involved. He is unaware of the resistance offered by oligarchies to the spread of knowledge among the people. This is another aspect of the truth, without which the halting progress of enlightenment cannot be understood either in the ancient or in the modern world.

Readers of Collet's *History of the Taxes on Knowledge*[4] will understand the problem as it existed in England in the nineteenth century, and will be able to set in its historical context the famous inscription on the *Examiner* newspaper in the 1830's: "Paper and print 3½d., Taxes on Knowledge 3½d., Price 7d." Then, "learning that the State," in the phrase of George Jacob Holyoake, "was for a hundred and forty-three years the active and determined frustrator of public information," they will turn back to the study of the oligarchical policies of Greece and Rome with a sharpened comprehension. In the view of the present writer, the problem of government in the class-divided societies of classical antiquity reveals its acuteness not only in the descriptions of open *stasis*, or class-warfare, in which the ✓ records of the ancient historians abound, but in the systematic efforts on the part of governments, priesthoods, and leaders of thought in various fields of human achievement, to provide the mass of their people not with true ideas but with "wholesome" ones.

[1] For Joannes Philoponus see Brunet et Mieli, *Histoire des Sciences: Antiquité*, Paris, 1935, pp. 963 ff. It may be noted that the opinion of these two authorities is wholly against the out-moded view that Christianity killed Greek science. According to them it died of internal decay. *Elle aurait eu le même sort, croyons-nous, sans l'intervention de l'église chrétienne* (p. 978).

[2] See Seignobos, in his recent *Essai d'une Histoire Comparée des Peuples de l'Europe* (Rieder, Paris, 1938), p. 29: Les Grecs, opérant sur les connaissances accumulées en Orient créèrent une methode de pensée si nouvelle qu'elle a été appelée "le miracle grec" et attribuée à un génie propre à la race hellénique. En fait, elle fut l'œuvre d'un petit nombre d'individus, savants, philosophes, écrivains, venus des points les plus éloignés, la plupart même de pays dont la population n'était d'origine hellénique.

[3] See Salomon Reinach's *Orpheus*, English translation, Routledge, 1931, pp. 24 and 95.

[4] Collet's *History of the Taxes on Knowledge*, Watts (Thinker's Library), Intro. pp. x and xi.

CHAPTER THREE

A SECOND GLANCE AT OUR PROBLEM

THE GEOMETER-GOD

In this chapter it appears that arithmetic is democratic, geometry oligarchic, and that God prefers the latter.

Science, as has been implied in our last chapter, can advance or retreat along two roads. There is first the advance that consists in the actual progress of knowledge and refinement of ideas, irrespective of the numbers of those who share in the advance. In the second place there is the progress of the dissemination of scientific ideas among the general mass of the people.

In our modern world, where the practical applications of science have transformed and continue to transform society, the question of the dissemination of scientific knowledge among the people at large assumes a different aspect from that which it presented in antiquity. Pure science, in our western democracies, may still to some extent be the preserve of an oligarchy, but without a wide dissemination of technical knowledge modern society is unworkable. The problem that presents itself to societies of oligarchical complexion is how to combine political ignorance with technical efficiency.

These considerations reveal to us the further fact that there is a connection between the character of science and its dissemination. In this matter our democracies are at the

26

cross-roads. Either our science must transform itself by the recognition that the history of its development is unintelligible without an understanding of its social origins; that men cannot be adequately trained in applied science without instruction in its social function; and that the obstacles to the progress of science can be external to it, in the sense that they rise out of the structure of society as well as out of theoretical errors; either this transformation must take place or science must retreat. The future of science is now plainly a political question. Either we must base our civilization more thoroughly on scientific foundations, or we must destroy science itself. Both processes are taking place in the world to-day.

But in the world of Classical Antiquity, though there was an analogous situation, it had recognizable differences. The machine age had not come. At the basis of the social pile lay man himself, not man and the machine. There was therefore no problem to be solved of combining technical training with political incompetence. The problem was the simpler one of disseminating such ideas as would make the unjust distribution of the rewards and toils of life seem a necessary part of the eternal constitution of things, and of suppressing such ideas as might lead to criticism of this view of the universe. That the extent to which this political principle operated seriously conditioned the history of science, and was, in fact, a major cause of that degeneration of science which took place between Anaximander and Cosmas Indicopleustes, it is the object of this essay to prove.

There will be those who will deny that any such considerations affected the judgments of leaders of thought and opinion in Classical Antiquity. There will be many more, who though they will admit that there is some evidence for this contention, will think that it is of little or no moment. This must be so, otherwise it is difficult to account for the fact that they make so little mention of it in their books. The usual practice is to affirm, or to assume without affirming, that the opinions of all ancient thinkers are innocent of any other consideration than devotion to Truth. It will be well therefore to give an example of what is meant by the contention that both the character of ancient science and the problem of its dissemination were affected by political considerations.

In the Eighth Book of Plutarch's *Dinner-table Discussions*, the second topic raised is Plato's meaning in saying, if he did say, that *God is always busy with geometry*. Diogenianus raises the question, and after a preliminary assent has been given to Plutarch's view that the saying, though not to be found in any of the writings of Plato, is certainly conformable to the spirit and style of the man, the discussion begins. The first speaker, Tyndares, is not disposed to see any special difficulty in the saying. Are we to suppose, he asks, that Plato meant anything more unusual or subtle than his oft-repeated opinion that the function of geometry is to draw us away from the sensible and the perishable to the intelligible and the eternal? For the contemplation of the eternal is the end of philosophy, as the contemplation of the mysteries is the end of initiation. We must remember, he says, that it was for this reason that Plato found fault with the attempts of Eudoxus, Archytas, and Menaechmus to find solutions for geometrical problems by instrumental and mechanical devices. For these bring us down to material things again, and away from the eternal and bodiless Forms with which God, being God, is always occupied.

(So spoke Tyndares. And I think we may take it that it is generally, if still not universally, admitted that this shrinking of Platonic science from contact with material things is not unconnected with the aristocratic contempt for manual labour. If further evidence should be wanted on this point, it can be found in those chapters of his *Life of Marcellus* in which Plutarch records with approval the contempt felt by the great engineer Archimedes for his own mechanical achievements.)

But the second speaker, Florus, was far from being content with this simple explanation. He thinks there may be something more particular implied. With pointed reference to the fact that Tyndares was a Lacedaemonian, he reminds the company that Plato was wont to link the name of his master Socrates with that of Lycurgus the law-giver of Sparta; indeed that he looked upon the founder of the Spartan constitution as being as important an influence on Socrates as the mathematician Pythagoras himself. He then offers the following remarkable interpretation of Plato's conception of the geometer-God. "Lycurgus is said to have banished the study of arithmetic from Sparta, as being democratic and popular in its effect, and to have introduced geometry, as being better suited to a sober oligarchy and constitutional monarchy. For arithmetic, by its employment of number, distributes things equally; geometry, by the employment of proportion, distributes things according to merit. Geometry is therefore not a source of confusion in the State, but has in it a notable principle of distinction between good men and bad, who are awarded their portions not by weight or lot, but by the difference between vice and virtue. This, the geometrical, is the system of proportion which God applies to affairs. This it is, my dear Tyndares, which is called by the names of *Dike* and *Nemesis*, and which teaches us that we ought to regard justice as equality, but not equality as justice. For what the many aim at is the greatest of all injustices, and God has removed it out of the world as being unattainable; but he protects and maintains the distribution of things according to merit, determining it geometrically, that is in accordance with proportion and law."

(The equation between Spartan oligarchy, geometry, and the law of God, may seem surprising to some. We shall unhappily be familiar enough with such thoughts before we have finished our enquiry.)

The third speaker, Autobulus, was not quite satisfied with what Florus had said. To him it seemed that Plato had intended something less political and more cosmic in significance. What Plato intended to convey is that Matter is a principle of disorder and discord on which geometry imposes order and harmony. For "when number and proportion are put into Matter, then the indeterminate is bound and circumscribed, first by lines, next by surfaces and depths, and so furnishes the first forms and different bodily shapes which serve as the foundation and base, as it were, for the coming into being of air and earth, of water and fire."

When Plutarch himself, who spoke last, was asked to make his contribution, he expressed himself as of the opinion that there was something in what each of them had said. He rejected neither the ethical view that the function of geometry is to lift up our minds from things earthly to things heavenly; nor the political view that geometry is oligarchic, and arithmetic democratic; nor the cosmic view, that an understanding of the principles of geometry is the key to the understanding of the universe, the view that exalts *a priori* mathematics above observational physics; he rejected none of these views but rather summed them all up in a religious interpretation of his own.

30

God, according to Plutarch's interpretation of Plato's meaning, being the supreme geometer, had set himself, in the act of creation, the supreme geometrical problem. This is not, as might be supposed, the demonstration that the square on the hypotenuse of a right-angled triangle is equal to the sum of the squares on the other two sides; rather was it that altogether choicer problem, on finding the solution to which Pythagoras had felt moved to sacrifice to God. This was: Given any two figures, construct a third similar to one and the same size as the other. The universe, Plutarch explained, owed its origin to three things, God, Matter, and Form. Matter is of all subject things the most disorderly; Form is of all patterns the fairest; God is of all causes the best. God, therefore, set Himself the problem to make a third thing like Form and coextensive with Matter. The result was the Kosmos, in which Form is imposed on all Matter.

So ends this particular Dinner-table Discussion. It is obvious that it comes out of a rich culture. And when we remember that some five hundred years separate Plutarch from Plato we are reminded of the vitality of that culture. The Academy which Plato had founded was still alive and was not to be closed for another four hundred years. We cannot but be impressed with the tenacity as well as the intellectual content of the Platonic tradition. But, equally, nobody can pretend that the system has not got a political side to it. It is the philosophy of an oligarch. The ethics, the science, the religion are quite consciously held as part of the creed of an oligarch. Or, if one prefers to put it the other way, the political theory of oligarchy is held to be the necessary consequence of the ethical, scientific, and religious views.

Furthermore, one cannot but be struck with the emphasis

upon mathematical, and the neglect of physical, science. Again, even within the domain of mathematics it is possible for one branch of the subject to be felt to be oligarchical and another democratic. And not only is arithmetic condemned as having egalitarian tendencies; mechanics are rejected as a danger to the soul. Amidst prejudices so violent as these, is it not possible, or even probable, that the neglect of physics is a further example of the influence of politics on science? That this is indeed so we shall attempt to show in the sequel. And the consequences of its neglect were neither slight nor soon mended. They were, in a famous phrase with which we shall be concerned later, "wounds of life," the occasion of groaning and tears to many generations of men.

CHAPTER FOUR

A THIRD GLANCE AT OUR PROBLEM

FROM EMPEDOCLES TO PRUDENTIUS

In the fifth century B.C. the pagan poet Empedocles preaches the need for a knowledge of the Nature of Things. In the fifth century A.D., the Christian poet Prudentius rejects the knowledge of the Nature of Things.

In discussing the history of science even in modern times it is far from easy to be certain how far the dissemination of ideas among the public has kept pace with the progress of knowledge in itself. This information is still more difficult to acquire with regard to ancient times. And in speaking of the high level of scientific knowledge attained by Anaximander in Miletus in the middle of the sixth century we intended no guarantee that his ideas had permeated society widely and deeply.

Nevertheless, there is much evidence in support of the view that the Ionian renaissance was in a very real sense a popular movement of enlightenment. Thus in a medical treatise on *The Nature of Man*, which dates from the second half of the fifth century, we have evidence of a wide interest in the science of the day. The writer opens with the remark: "He who is in the habit of listening to speakers who discuss the nature of man in a way that goes beyond its connexion with the science of medicine will find nothing to interest him in the present account." Then, after a few acid comments on the random speculations of philosophers who discuss human nature without a study of medicine, the writer observes that the fact that they contradict one another is proof that their approach is at fault, and proceeds: "One can easily convince himself of this by attending their debates. Though the same debaters appear again and again before the same audiences, no one ever wins three times in succession. Now one is victorious now another, the popular favour going to the talker who displays the readiest eloquence before the crowd."

The evidence for a wide popular interest in the most advanced physical speculations of the day seems conclusive. And this becomes the more impressive if it is remembered that the philosophical opinions attacked by the Ionian medical writer are those of the poet-philosopher, Empedocles of Acragas in Sicily. Empedocles was probably still alive when the treatise from which we have been quoting was written. It is startling testimony to the permeation of the Greek world of the fifth century by philosophic and scientific ideas that the views of a Sicilian poet should be the rage with popular audiences in the lecture halls of Asia Minor, and should provoke an acrid discussion by an Asiatic doctor.

Further evidence of the impact of the scientific thought of the day on society in general is provided if we turn to the mainland of Greece. Before the vast audiences in the theatre of Dionysus at Athens the choruses were already chanting lyrics in which Euripides was introducing to his somewhat backward fellow-citizens the views of the Ionian thinkers which he had learned from Anaxagoras, their representative in Athens. And already, before Empedocles, two philosophic poets of considerable powers had appeared, one in Asia Minor, one in Italy. These were Xenophanes and Parmenides. And their choice of verse for a medium is sure proof that they intended their utterances to reach a wide audience. Xenophanes, we know, gave public recitations of his poetry, and in his old age he could boast that his thought had already been sixty-five years in circulation throughout the world of Greece. What was the specific quality of this new and exciting knowledge?

Among the fragments of verse by Xenophanes that have come down to us are two lines in which he says that "the Gods have not revealed everything to men from the beginning, but men by searching in time find out better." This is in the true spirit of the age. But as men became conscious of knowledge as a slow accumulation of experience acquired by active search they became curious also to understand the nature of knowledge and the process by which it is acquired. Thus opened the great debate on the validity of the information conveyed to us by the senses, and on the part played by Reason in the constitution of human knowledge. The second poet of whom we have spoken, Parmenides, convinced, by many proofs, of the fallibility of the senses, was of opinion that Reason alone could be relied on, and endeavoured to construct a system of philosophy from which the evidence of the senses should be ejected.

Empedocles, although the doctors scented danger to their science from the too hasty application of his theories, was a true scientist as well as a philosopher and a poet; and he took a middle course. He was too wise to reject the evidence of the senses. If he did not regard sense evidence as in itself science, he knew that it was the material of science; and he knew that it was by reflection on the evidence of the senses that advance in physical knowledge is made. He himself was responsible for one of the major advances in early science, namely the experimental demonstration of the corporeal nature of the invisible air. Accordingly it is not surprising that one of the best passages in his poem (of which considerable fragments survive) is that in which, admitting the shortness of human life, the narrow limits of human knowledge, and the treachery of the senses, he exhorts men to make every use of sense evidence, as being the only source of information they possess. Then, having cleared the ground by this discussion of the theory of knowledge, he proceeds to sing his poem "On the Nature of Things," in the course of which he expounds a system which still influences popular language in the present day—the theory that all things are made up of the four elements, Earth, Air, Fire, and Water, attracted towards one another or repelled from one another by the forces of Love and Hate.

In this new and passionate interest in Nature, in *Physis*, which manifested itself in debates in the lecture hall, in the tragic performances at Athens, in didactic poems publicly recited, we witness, as is universally agreed by all competent authorities, a revolution of thought. These new ideas were not born *in vacuo*. They did not find men's minds empty of previous views and ready to accept the new outlook on the universe without question. On the contrary the new views could only make their way if they could succeed in driving out another view of things. The new view talked of such things as Earth, Fire, Air, and Water, and forces of Love and Hate, and, what was still more original, offered no authority in support of such views other than the arguments of their originator or supporter, and no inducement to believe them other than a passion for truth. The older view had peopled the world with gods and demi-gods and supernatural beings of various sorts; offered in support of a belief in their existence not arguments but tradition; and held out, as an inducement to belief, the favour which a satisfied god, demi-god, or other spirit could show a mortal with whom It was pleased, or the injury It could do if It were vexed. Further, the older view was knit into the fabric of society and the constitution of the State, for which in a multitude of ways it constituted a sanction and support. The new views had to encounter, therefore, not only, nor even mainly, intellectual opposition. They encountered the dead weight of tradition, the uneasy disapproval of society, the covert and powerful hostility of vested interest. That it was such forces as these that availed to strangle physical speculation so shortly after its birth will be argued in later chapters. But first we ask leave to exhibit by the contrast between Empedocles and Prudentius, as we sought to do before by the contrast between Anaximander and Cosmas Indicopleustes, what precisely we mean by the strangling of physical speculation, the elimination from the mental make-up of an age of a concern for a knowledge of The Nature of Things.

Prudentius is a figure of extraordinary interest. Born, probably in Spain, in the middle of the fourth century of our era, he had a distinguished public career as lawyer, judge, and governor. But having scaled the ladder of public ambition in the service of the Emperor he came, at the height of his career, to transfer his allegiance to Christ and to regard all his successful service of the Emperor as so much waste of time.

"Quidvis utile tanti spatio temporis egimus?"
("Did I do anything useful in all that time?")

he asks in an admirable poem in which from his new Christian standpoint he looks back upon his official achievement. It was Christianity that made Prudentius a poet. His

37

life as an active administrator had been rendered to Caesar, now in his grey hairs he could render to God only the offering of song. But what an offering! It can rarely have been given to any man to attain to such distinction in two spheres. Who else commenced poet so late and reached to such heights?

> "Quid generosa potest anima,
> Lucis et aetheris indigena,
> Solvere dignius obsequium,
> Quam data munera si recinat
> Artificem modulata suum?"[1]
>
> *Hymn III*, 31–35.

His poetic achievement falls into two great divisions, the hymns and the didactic poems. In the hymns it is as if the parched soil of the pagan classical tradition had been fertilized by innumerable rills from the new springs of hope in the Gospel and had blossomed in a thousand flowers as in his own vision of heaven, where "the ground was purple with sweet-smelling roses and poured forth in profusion fat marigolds, drooping violets, and slim crocuses":

> "Illic purpureis tecta rosariis
> omnis fraglat humus caltaque pinguia
> et molles violas et tenues crocos
> fundit fonticulis uda fugacibus."
>
> *Hymn V*, 113–116.

For Prudentius the oracles of Zion had taken the place of Delphi and the Sibylline books, and, in succession to the mythology of Greece which time had rendered stale if not incredible, the story of Israel offered a fair field for faith and poetry, while the mild injunctions of the Sermon on the Mount usurped the room of the imperialistic exhortations (*parcere subjectis et debellare superbos*) of the Roman poet.

Who could fail to be charmed at meeting apostolic counsels
of charity clothed in the style of the fables of Phaedrus:

> "Est quippe et illud grande virtutis genus,
> operire nudos, indigentes pascere,
> opem benignam ferre supplicantibus,
> unam paremque sortis humanae vicem
> inter potentes atque egenos ducere."
>
> *Hymn VII*, 211–215.

("This too is a great type of virtue, to clothe the naked,
feed the hungry, give help to those who ask it, and to regard
both rich and poor as men.")

Or at finding the bidding of Jesus, that one who fasts should
be kempt and clean, repeated in graceful Sapphics:

> "Addit et, ne quis velit invenusto
> sordidus cultu lacerare frontem,
> sed decus vultus capitisque pexum
>   comat honorem:
>
> 'Terge ieiunans,' ait, 'omne corpus
> neve subducto faciem rubore
> luteus tinguat color aut notetur
>   pallor in ore'"?
>
> *Hymn VIII*, 21–28.

Nor in the handling of some of the miraculous incidents
in the Old or New Testament is there much to disturb one.
Daniel in the lions' den may provoke a smile:

> "O semper pietas fidesque tuta!
> lambunt indomiti virum leones;"
>
> *Hymn IV*, 43, 44.

Yet who could fail to be indulgent to the pious emphasis
of that apt alliteration, "the *l*ions *l*icked him"? And when
Jacob wrestles with the angel, the image is presented with

such monumental force and simplicity, and the moral significance of the incident is so grandly conveyed, that one gladly allows to the poet the praise which he often merits, that he touches the sublime:

"Sub nocte Iacob caerula,
luctator audax angeli,
eo usque dum lux surgeret,
sudavit impar proelium."[2]

Hymn II, 73–76.

A similar felicity and inspiration inform much of the great Ninth Hymn in celebration of the miracles of Christ. Consider, for instance, the description of the miracle of the walking on the water:

"Ambulat per stagna ponti, summa calcat fluctuum,
mobilis liquor profundi pendulam praestat viam
nec fatiscit unda sanctis pressa sub vestigiis."

49–51.

("He walks over the pools of the sea, and treads the tops of the waves; the moving waves of the deep afford a floating path, and the billow holds beneath the sacred steps.")

One cannot but note the brilliance of the *pendulam* and the effect of its juxtaposition with *profundi*, not to speak of the swing and heave of the rhythm. But it is in the last verse of this poem that Prudentius achieves one of his most remarkable triumphs:

"Fluminum lapsus et undae, litorum crepidines,
imber, aestus, nix, pruina, silva et aura, nox, dies,
omnibus te concelebrent saeculorum saeculis."

("Gliding river, splashing shore, rain, sun, snow, frost, leaf and breeze, night, day, shall praise Thee for ever and ever.")

The Latin language has never been used to better effect. The first line is a miracle of sound, the gliding river and the splashing shore each magically rendered and made more pleasing in their contrast. When a man has achieved a line like that first, awakening all our senses and sensibilities by the alertness of his own, he may then venture safely on one of those bare enumerations of the names of natural things (which Latin literature affected before Walt Whitman) in the confident hope that it has been transformed into something more than an enumeration, that it has become a delight in the varied aspects of nature shared between reader and poet. But how much more than this Prudentius has done! First we have association by contrast (*imber* and *aestus*), as in the opening line. Then, lest even the thought pattern should weary us, association by likeness (*nix*, *pruina*). These associations are given by the mere juxtaposition of the words; but the next (*silva et aura*) is expressed formally by the visible link of the conjunction, and for a reason. The two form a single idea, "the wind in the leaves," as surely as the two that follow (*nox*, *dies*), "night, day," must not be verbally linked since in reality they cannot coexist but must alternate.

But if such be the arts by which Prudentius can blind us to much that is infantile in his intelligence, there are times when his total subjection to the miraculous is an offence to one who yearns to pay him the homage of a full respect. When he comes, for instance, to Elijah and his fiery chariot, or the adventures of Jonah, he allows no quarter to those who cannot share his faith, or his credulity. Here is his description of Jonah in the belly of the whale. The matter-of-fact vividness is characteristic:

"Ternis dierum ac noctium processibus
mansit ferino devoratus gutture,
errabat illic per latebras viscerum,
ventris meandros circumibat tortiles
anhelus extis intus aestuantibus."

Hymn VII, 121-125.

("Full three days and three nights he remained within
after he had been swallowed by the monster, wandering
there through the dark lairs of the flesh, making his winding
way through the tortuous twists of the belly, panting in
the sultry heat of the organs within.")

For when Prudentius believes in a miracle, and if it is a
Jewish or a Christian one, he always believes in it, he has
no reserves. Thus in his didactic poem, *The Birth of Sin,*
with a brief consideration of which we shall conclude our
analysis of the poet, he refers to the turning of Lot's wife
into a pillar of salt and describes the miracle in the following
terms:

"Traxerat Evva virum dirae ad consortia culpae,
haec peccans sibi sola perit: solidata metallo
diriguit fragili saxumque liquabile facta
stat mulier, sicut steterat prius, omnia servans,
caute sigillati longum salis effigiata,
et decus et cultum frontemque oculosque co-
mamque
et flexam in tergum faciem paulumque relata
menta retro, antiquae monumenta rigentia noxae.
liquitur illa quidem salsis sudoribus uda,
sed nulla ex fluido plenae dispendia formae
sentit deliquio, quantumque armenta saporum
attentuant saxum, tantum lambentibus umor
sufficit attritamque cutem per damna reformat.

42

hoc meruit titulo peccatrix femina sisti
infirmum fluidumque animum per lubrica solvens
consilia et fragilis iussa ad caelestia."

Hamartigenia, 741 ff.

("Eve had involved her lord in her fault; Lot's wife
wrought only her own destruction. Solidified into a fragile
substance, she stiffened, yea, transformed to melting stone
the woman stood, as she had stood before, moulded into a
tall column of statuesque salt, but preserving every feature,
the ornament, the dress, the brow, the eyes, the hair, the
backward glance, the turned chin, a motionless memorial
of her former sin. True indeed she drips and runs in salt
sweat, but from all that liquid flow knows no impairment
of her perfect form. True, the cattle thin the savoury salt
rock, but, as they lick, fresh moisture is supplied to repair
the damage to her worn skin. For she deserved to stand
as a monument of sinful woman, too weak for the commands of heaven, dissolving in her melting counsels the
infirm and fluid will.")

So serious is the poet that there can be no doubt it would
have been a shock to his faith if he had visited the scene
and not found Lot's wife listed in the local guide-book
among the monuments of interest.

No doubt it is the grossness of such credulity that has
turned modern readers aside from the study of Prudentius
and deprived them of acquaintance with such powerful and
interesting passages as those in which he attacks the games,
the state cults (*idololatrix religio*), the greed of the wealthy
landowners, and the vanity of ambition. Neither in manner
nor in matter do these things fall below the best of Juvenal.
But they cannot detain us now. Our purpose is to enquire
how such all-round intelligence can coexist with such total

43

ignorance of the Nature of Things, and such hostility to the acquisition of this kind of knowledge.

For this is the point to be seized. Prudentius is in general neither ignorant nor incurious. Far from it. It is not only that he is cultured in the legal or the literary sense. He is capable also of such incursion into the theory of numbers as may suffice to establish his view of the doctrine of the Trinity.[3]

But when it comes to physics the atittude is changed. To borrow any information from Natural Philosophy, though it be no more dangerous than an illustration from the habits of a member of the animal kingdom, is to be sensible of the need for an apology:

"si licet ex ethnicis quidquam praesumere, vel si de physicis exempli aliquid . . ."

Op. cit., 581, 2.

("If it be allowed to borrow anything from the heathen, or take an illustration from the Natural Philosophers. . . .")

It is in the attitude to a knowledge of Nature that we find the change between Empedocles and Prudentius, between the poet of the fifth century before Christ and the poet of the fifth century after. The change is the same as that which we observed in the transition from Anaximander to Cosmas Indicopleustes. In this case it is perhaps all the more impressive. For while Cosmas as a thinker is quite unable to sustain comparison with Anaximander, Prudentius is at least as great a poet as Empedocles. It is the mental climate that is different, not the individual men. Nor should it be thought that the change from Empedocles to Prudentius is all loss. Prudentius, the heir of three traditions, those of Israel, Greece, and Rome; the man in whose spirit the sentiment of the Gospels had wrestled with the Roman tradition of government and overthrown it; the

44

Roman lyrist who, on any just estimate, must form a third with Catullus and Horace; the satirist, who is greater than Persius and can stand comparison with Juvenal; this man Prudentius can offer us a richness and complexity of culture that make the verses of Empedocles appear rude and uncouth. And yet, for the lack of a true approach to Nature, Prudentius is as certainly a herald of darkness as Empedocles is of the dawn.

For the age of Prudentius had lost its way in the world. He belonged to the generation who were learning from St. Augustine and others that the Holy Scriptures, when they speak of natural things, are infallible, and that, consequently, when there is contradiction between Nature and the Bible we must correct our ideas of Nature in accordance with the Bible, not the Bible in accordance with Nature. This view is destructive of all natural science and of all history. When it had triumphed every other victory of darkness followed in its train. Modern science has only revived again in so far as it has step by step contested the ground with this view of the world.

If it be true, as Dr. George Sarton maintains, that "the great intellectual division of mankind is not along geographical or racial lines, but between those who understand and practice the experimental method and those who do not understand and do not practice it," then the division can be applied vertically to history as well as horizontally to the modern world. And from this point of view the three great intellectual divisions of European history are the pre-Socratic movement in Greek philosophy, during which the possibility of a natural knowledge of the universe was glimpsed and the conditions of its attainment defined; the long period of two thousand years from Plato to Galileo, in which this knowledge was first lost and then slowly

45

recovered; and the modern and contemporary epoch, which across that gap of two thousand years is linked with the Ionian dawn. Plato was a great intellect; but when he based education on mathematics instead of on Natural Philosophy he led the world astray. St. Augustine was a mighty spirit; but when he taught "Whatever knowledge man has acquired outside Holy Writ, if it be harmful it is there condemned; if it be wholesome, it is there contained," he was destroying the sign-posts. The next thousand years did not contain a better intellect than that of St. Thomas; but when he said that we must believe the assertions of the Prophets *etiamsi pertineant ad conclusiones scientiarum* (even if they have reference to the conclusions of science), he was still barring the way to human progress.

Of the disastrous consequences of substituting revelation for observation Prudentius is tragic proof. Despising natural knowledge he is full of strange supernatural doctrines confidently held. He knows that the origin of evil in the world is due to a Fallen Spirit. He knows that this Fallen Spirit brought about the corruption of mankind. And he knows that it is the corruption of mankind that has brought about the corruption of nature. If there are weeds, beasts of prey, poisonous plants, and perturbations of the elements such as storms, it is because man has sinned. To quote his conclusion of the argument:

> "nec mirum, si membra orbis concussa rotantur,
> si vitiis agitata suis mundana laborat
> machina, si terras luis incentiva fatigat:
> exemplum dat vita hominum, quo cetera peccent."
> *Op. cit.*, 247–250.

("It is no wonder if the parts of the wheeling universe are shaken and loosened, if the world machine is vexed by

its own defects and threatens to break down, if a wearisome
pestilence plagues the earth: it is the life of men that sets
the example which has corrupted the rest of creation.")

How different this wisdom is from Natural Philosophy
needs no urging.

Other problems of human destiny are settled with an
equal confidence in the light of the same wisdom. If one
enquires whether, and in what sense, man is free, this
question is not answered in the light of a knowledge of
human nature and its place in Nature as a whole. It is
answered by the logic of the law-courts applied to Biblical
facts:

> "an, cum te dominum cunctis, quaecumque crearat,
> praeficeret mundumque tuis servire iuberet
> imperiis, cumque arva, polum, mare, flumina, ventos
> dederet arbitrium de te tibi credere avarus
> nollet ut indigno libertatemque negaret?"
>
> *Op. cit.*, 679–683.

("Or, seeing that He had made you lord of all creation
and bid the world be obedient to your commands, seeing
that He had surrendered to you the earth, the sky, the sea,
the streams, the winds, would He have been so niggard
as to refuse you power over yourself, as unworthy, and
to deny you liberty?")

When this kind of knowledge is confidently held it is
generally guaranteed by something more than argument.
Prudentius is precisely informed of the eternal lot after this
life of the Blessed and the Damned. For this knowledge
he makes no apology; it was not borrowed from any pagan
Natural Philosopher. Let us first accompany him to Hell:

"praescius inde pater liventia tartara plumbo
incendit liquido piceasque bitumine fossas
infernalis aquae furvo subfodit Averno
et Flegetonteo sub gurgite sanxit edaces
perpetuis scelerum poenis inolescere vermes.
norat enim flatu ex proprio vegetamen inesse
corporibus nostris animamque ex ore perenni
formatam non posse mori, non posse vicissim
pollutam vitiis rursum ad convexa reverti
mersandam penitus puteo ferventis abyssi.
vermibus et flammis et discruciatibus aevum
immortale dedit, senio ne poena periret,
non pereunte anima: carpunt tormenta foventque
materiem sine fine datam, mors deserit ipsa
aeternos gemitus et flentes vivere cogit."

Op. cit., 824–838.

("It was to meet this need that the Father kindled a glowing hell of molten lead, and dug beneath grim Acheron trenches of smoking pitch for the infernal streams, and decreed that under Phlegethon's pool hungry worms should breed as a perpetual punishment for sin. For He knew that there was in our bodies, from His own breath, a principle of life, and that souls formed by His immortal mouth could not die; nor could they, on the other hand, polluted with their sin, return to the sky, but must rather be plunged deep in the bottomless burning pit. So to the worms and to the flames and to the tortures He gave undying life, that the punishment might not grow old and die when the soul does not die: therefore the torments both vex and restore the matter that fails not for ever; death herself deserts the eternal groans and compels the sinners to live and weep.")

But if Hell be ugly, Heaven is uglier still:

"illic purpureo latus exporrecta cubili
floribus aeternis spirantes libat odores
ambrosiumque bibit roseo de stramine rorem
ditibus et longo fumantibus intervallo
fluminaque et totos caeli sitientibus imbres
inplorata negat digitum insertare palato
flammarumque apices umenti extinguere tactu."

Op. cit., 856–862.

("There the soul stretched on its side upon a purple couch
draws in the odours that breathe from eternal blossoms,
sips, on its bed of roses, ambrosial dew, and, beholding
the rich men smoking at a great distance and thirsting for
rivers and all the rains of heaven, though oft implored
it still refuses to insert even the tip of its finger within
the mouth and check the dancing flames with its moist
touch.")

The question of the possibility of the soul stretching its
arm from Heaven to Hell ought to have been raised by our
theological poet; for that he takes the possibility literally
seems proved by the demonstration in supernatural optics
that follows at once, by which he proves that the *eye* of
the soul will certainly be able to see all the way from the
abode of bliss to the abode of damnation:

"nec mirere locis longe distantibus inter
damnatas iustasque animas concurrere visus
conspicuos meritasque vices per magna notari
intervalla, polus medio quae dividit orbe.
errat, quisque animas nostrorum fine oculorum
aestimat, involvit vitreo quos lucida palla
obice, quis speculum concreta coagula texunt
impediuntque vagas obducto umore fenestras.

numne animarum oculis denso vegetamine guttae
volvuntur teretes aut palphebralibus extra
horrescunt saetis ciliove umbrante teguntur?
illis viva acies nec pupula parva sed ignis
traiector nebulae vasti et penetrator operti est."

Op. cit., 863–875.

("And be not surprised that clear vision can run over the great spaces that divide the damned souls from the just, and that the due rewards of each can be observed at such an interval as is formed by the whole span of the sky. For that man is in error who seeks to judge of souls by the limitations of our mortal sight. Our eyes are wrapped in a transparent coat which forms for them a glassy obstacle; massed curd weaves for them their optic mirror and blocks those roving windows with a veil of moisture. But are we to suppose that from the eyes of the soul, which are packed full with life, round tears can fall, or that they are hedged outside with a fringe of lashes on the lids, or obscured by shady brows? No, theirs is the living vision, no small pupil but a fire which leaps through mists and penetrates the vastest obstacles.")

After these painful evidences of the corruption of intelligence and character possible in a great man whose mind has lost its way in the world, what consolation is it that in the magic of his verse are evidences also of new and trembling sensitivities born of the travail of his bewildered spirit? The trumpets of the Day of Wrath are already sounding in his ears and he can thrill us with anticipations of the harmonies of Thomas of Celano:

"tristes et percipit aure
mugitus gravium mundi sub fine tubarum."

Op. cit., 916, 7.

50

But we long for one touch of the wisdom of which Walt Whitman said that "There is something in the float of the sight of *things* that provokes it out of the soul."

---

[1] The magic of this verse vanishes in translation. The literal English equivalent is : *Can the noble soul, native to light and air, pay any worthier service than if it sing the blessings that have been given it, taking its Creator as its theme?* But this gives no sense of the quick vital pulse of the rhythm, and the combination of simplicity and appropriateness in the choice of words.

[2] The literal translation of this verse is : *Beneath the purple night Jacob, the bold wrestler with the angel, sweated in unequal combat even until light should rise.* But it is quite untranslatable. The resources of the Latin language are exploited by a master. There is not a better verse in Catullus or Horace. With its monumental force is combined a perfection of vowel and consonant music which make of it a miracle of sound. The position of the name *Iacob* between *nocte* and *caerula*, setting the hero of the picture against his background of sky; and the employment of alliteration to point the meaning (*audax angeli*), are further examples of the art of Prudentius.

[3]
> unus enim princeps numeri est nec dinumerari
> tantum unus potis est, sic cum pater ac deus alter
> non sit, item Christus non sit genitore secundus,
> anterior numero est, cui filius unicus uni est.
> ille deus meritoque deus, quia primus et unus,
> in virtute sua primus, tum primus in illo,
> quem genuit; quid enim differt generatio simplex?
> *Hamartigenia*, 36–44.

I am not competent to say whether this is good mathematics; but at least it serves to make clear that the theologian in Prudentius did not see any necessity to quarrel with that abstract and *a priori* science.

CHAPTER FIVE

PAGAN AND CHRISTIAN
SUPERSTITION

An interlude, in which it is shown that Pagans, as well as Christians, if they despised the knowledge of the Nature of Things, became defenceless against superstition.

The fact that in the effort to define my problem I have chosen to contrast two pagan writers, distinguished for their rationalism, with two Christian writers who were notably superstitious, may lay me open to the imputation of regarding superstition as a Christian monopoly. This misunderstanding is the more likely since the contrast between Greek rationalism and Christian superstition has been a commonplace of rationalist writers.

In a well-known letter of Shelley's (to John Gisborne, November 16, 1819) we read:

"I envy you the first reading of Theocritus. Were not the Greeks a glorious people? What is there, as Job says of the Leviathan, like unto them? If the army of Nicias had not been defeated under the walls of Syracuse; if the Athenians had, acquiring Sicily, held the balance between Rome and Carthage, sent garrisons to the Greek colonies in the South of Italy, Rome might have been all that its intellectual condition entitled it to be, a tributary, not the conqueror of Greece; the Macedonian power would never have attained to the dictatorship of the civilized States of the world. Who knows whether, under the steady progress which philosophy and social institutions would have made (for, in the age to which I refer, their progress was both rapid and secure), among a people of the most perfect physical organization, whether the Christian religion would have arisen, or the barbarians have overwhelmed the wrecks of civilization which had survived the conquest and the tyranny of the Romans? What then should we have been? As it is, all of us who are worth anything spend our manhood in unlearning the follies, or expiating the mistakes, of our youth. We are stuffed full of prejudices; and our natural passions are so managed, that if we restrain them we grow intolerant and precise, because we restrain them not according to reason, but according to error; and if we do not restrain them we do all sorts of mischief to ourselves and others. Our imagination and our understanding are alike subject to rules the most absurd. So much for Theocritus and the Greeks."

This, which we may call the eighteenth-century view of the matter, for it was thence that Shelley derived it, is certainly not true. The Christians were not more superstitious than their contemporaries, and they were much more alive. Contempt for the superstition of their pagan contemporaries is a commonplace in the writings of the early Christians, and they were entitled to it. The Christian writers of the second, third, and fourth centuries are on the whole superior to their pagan contemporaries in vitality, humanity, and sense. When the Emperor Julian restored paganism for a brief spell he was restoring an amalgam of superstitions which, if they had prevailed, would have made the Dark Ages darker than they were. We shall have more to say on this head later; but as it is essential to obviate the possibility of misunderstanding on this point at this stage of our argument, we shall devote this short chapter to a consideration of what educated Platonic circles in the Christian era were capable of in the matter of superstition, without any help from the Christians.

In an earlier chapter we drew upon the Eighth Book of Plutarch's *Dinner-table Discussions*. Then we were concerned with the Second Topic raised, namely, what Plato might be supposed to have meant by his saying that *God is always busy with geometry*. We shall now turn to the First Topic, and shall not, I think, find it less informing.

The dinner at which the First Topic was discussed was held on the anniversary of Plato's birth. It was not unnatural, then, that there should be some preliminary conversation on remarkable coincidences in the dates of the births and deaths of famous persons. Diogenianus was of opinion that accident had approximated very closely to intelligent design in arranging that the birthday of Socrates, the older friend and teacher of Plato, should fall on the sixth of February, while that of the disciple fell on the seventh. And it was noted as remarkable, among other similar coincidences, that Alexander the Great and Diogenes the Cynic should have died on the same day; and that Pindar should have been born on the festival of the Pythian Apollo and lived to write hymns in his honour.

At this Florus (for the guests were much the same as on the occasion of the discussion on geometry) brought up a coincidence that was both more striking in itself and more apt to the occasion, to wit, that both Plato, the founder of the Academy, and Carneades, one of its most famous supporters, had been born on the same day as one another, which day (as those present could confirm, for they were priests and prophets of the god) was also the birthday of Apollo. The atmosphere being now prepared, the real topic is introduced, namely, the possibility of a human being having divine parentage. "Wherefore," continued Florus, "I am of opinion that those who ascribe to Apollo the begetting of Plato do no dishonour to the god, for as Apollo sent us Asclepius trained by Cheiron to cure our bodies, so he sent us Plato trained by Socrates to cure still greater sufferings and diseases." And therewith he reminded the company of the vision that had been sent to Plato's father Aristo in a dream, and the voice that had been heard forbidding him for the space of ten months to have carnal knowledge of his wife.

Tyndares the Lacedaemonian intervened at this point. "Then we may apply to Plato the words of the poet,

> of mortal man
> Seems he not son, but truly son of god.

Yet this point troubles me, whether to engender, no less than to be engendered, be not at variance with the incorruptibility of the deity. For this surely too is a change and a passion. Which doubtless Alexander had in mind when he said that he then felt most mortal and corruptible when he lay with a woman or when he slept. For sleep is a surrendering that comes out of weakness, and there is no generation without the passing of what is one's own into another, which is loss. On the other hand I am comforted when I find that Plato calls the unbegotten and eternal god the *father* and maker of the universe and of all other created things; for his meaning must be that they come into existence not by seed, but that god by some other power engenders in matter that vital principle by which it is altered and changed.

> The hen bird heeds not the wind's wanton play,
> But, lo, time passes and the bird must lay.[1]

And it would not surprise me if the fact were that a god does not engender by close contact like a man, but employs some intermediary and by some different sort of touch and dalliance prepares the mortal stock and fills it secretly with the divine birth. And this is not a myth that I have invented; for the Egyptians say that Apis is so begotten by the touch of the Moon (a male deity with the Egyptians). Generally speaking, Egyptian theology admits the intercourse of male gods with mortal women. But they do not admit the contrary, that a mortal man could get a goddess with child. For in their view the substance of divine beings consists of air and spirits and heats and liquidities."

Such was the capacity of the pagan Plutarch and his friends to assess the claims of Egyptian theology. They were quite prepared to accept the miraculous conception of Plato. It was certainly not the miraculous side of Christianity that could render it inacceptable to Academicians, at least by A.D. 100.

[1] Two lines from the *Oenomaus* of Sophocles. Nauck, T. G. F., *Soph.* 436. The reference is to the old fable of the wind-egg.

CHAPTER SIX

THE
TWO GREAT ACHIEVEMENTS
OF PRE-SOCRATIC SCIENCE

The Atomic Theory and Hippocratic Medicine. The war on superstition begins.

The two great achievements of Ionian science before Socrates may be described as the atomic theory of the constitution of matter, with the cosmology based on it, and Hippocratic medicine. Leucippus and Democritus, the creators of atomism, based their theories on a wide range of observation, but could not test the truth of their speculations directly by experiment. Their subject-matter was inaccessible to them. The atoms, on which their whole theory rested, were by definition too small to be the objects of sense-experience; sun, moon, and stars were inaccessible. There was as yet no telescope, no microscope, and no science of chemistry. Their atomism was therefore very different from the modern atomic theory. It was a speculation based on the observation of uncontrolled natural phenomena. The modern atomic theory, though it borrowed the concepts and language of the old Greek speculation, differed fundamentally in being based on data derived from controlled experiments in chemistry. It would not be correct, however, to say that the Greeks could not appreciate the difference between theory based on observation of natural phenomena over which they had no control, and theory based on experiment. It was just this difference that impressed itself on the Hippocratic doctors who had their material, namely, the bodies of their patients, under their hands. The doctors were fully conscious that every treatment they applied to a patient had its experimental as well as its humanitarian side. And they excluded from the method of their science the unverifiable hypotheses of the physicists.

It must not be supposed, however, that the ancient speculators on physics were unaware of the necessity of relating every conclusion as closely as they could to *physis*, or Nature, itself. They never lost sight of the fact that it was Nature they were attempting to understand. Heraclitus defined wisdom as the understanding of the way in which the universe works. The Pythagoreans were put in the way of their special theory of the nature of things by experimenting with the musical notes that can be drawn from taut strings, and relating the pitch of these notes to the length of the strings. Empedocles demonstrated the corporeal nature of air by thrusting a funnel into water with the upper end closed and showing that the water could not enter until the finger was removed and the enclosed air released. When Anaxagoras wished to demonstrate that the senses have a limit beyond which their accuracy cannot be trusted, he did so by taking two vessels, one filled with a white liquid and one with a black, and mixing them drop by drop until the eye could no longer discern any distinction between them. These and similar experiments show that they had taken the first step to a real technique of systematic experimental investigation, although they did not get very far with it.

As for the range of observation of natural phenomena (as distinct from consciously controlled phenomena) on which their conclusions were based, it is truly impressive. Let us adduce in illustration a passage of Lucretius:

"Now mark me: since I have taught that things cannot be born from nothing, cannot when begotten be brought back to nothing, that you may not haply begin in any shape to mistrust my words, because the first beginnings of things cannot be seen by the eyes, take moreover this list of bodies which you must yourself admit are in the number of things and cannot be seen. First of all the force of the wind when aroused beats on the harbours and whelms huge ships and scatters clouds. . . . Winds therefore sure enough are unseen bodies which sweep the seas, the lands, ay and the clouds of heaven, tormenting them and catching them up in sudden whirls. . . . Then again we perceive the different smells of things, yet never see them coming to our nostrils; nor do we behold heats nor can we observe cold with the eyes nor are we used to see voices. Yet all these things must consist of a bodily nature, since they are able to move the senses; for nothing but body can touch and be touched. Again clothes hung up on a shore which waves break upon become moist, and then get dry if spread out in the sun. Yet it has not been seen in what way the moisture of water has sunk into them nor again in what way this has been dispelled by heat. The moisture therefore is dispersed into small particles which the eyes are quite unable to see. Again after the revolution of many suns a ring on the finger is thinned on the under side by wearing, the dripping from the eaves hollows a stone, the bent ploughshare of iron imperceptibly decreases in the fields, and we behold the stone-paved streets worn down by the feet of the multitude; the brass statues too at the gates shew their right hands to be wasted by the touch of the numerous passers by who greet them. These things then we see are lessened, since they have been thus worn down; but what bodies depart at any given time the nature of vision has jealously shut out our eeing. Lastly the bodies which time and nature add to things little by little, constraining them to grow in due measure, no exertion of the eyesight can behold; and so too wherever things grow old by age and decay, and when rocks hanging over the sea are eaten away by the gnawing salt spray, you cannot see what they lose at any given moment. Nature therefore works by unseen bodies."[1]

Such was the method and such were the conclusions of the ancient physicists; and such was the knowledge on which Cosmas Indicopleustes and Prudentius turned their backs.

It can be no part of our purpose here to expound the ancient doctrine of Atomism. But it is relevant to insist that the steps by which this system was evolved, steps marked by the names of Thales, Anaximander, Anaximenes, Pythagoras, Parmenides, Zeno, Melissus, Empedocles, Anaxagoras, Leucippus and Democritus, still form an admirable introduction to scientific culture, an admirable training in rational thought. These names mark an epoch in the history of humanity. With them begins a new relation between man and his environment which, after long frustration and delay, is bearing its fruit in a fresh advance of mankind in our own day. This period gave to us for the first time in recorded history the picture of man behaving in a fully rational way in the face of nature, confident that the ways of nature were not past finding out, awed with the discovery of law in nature, freed from the superstition of animism, serene in his willing subjection to the law. The spell of this new type of man fell upon the poet Euripedes through his friendship with Anaxagoras, and he sang of it, in his choruses, to the Athenian democracy in accents that can still move us by their pregnant anticipation of what the spirit of science can mean for mankind:

> ὄλβιος ὅστις τῆσδ' ἱστορίας
> ἔσχε μάθησιν, μήτε πολιτῶν
> ἐπὶ πημοσύνας μήτ' εἰς ἀδίκους
> πράξεις ὁρμῶν,
> ἀλλ' ἀθανάτου καθορῶν φύσεως
> Κόσμον ἀγήρω, πῇ τε συνέστη
> καὶ ὅθεν καὶ ὅπως·
> τοῖς τοιούτοις οὐδέποτ' αἰσχρῶν
> ἔργων μελέτημα προσίζει.[2]

("Blessed is the man who has laid hold of the knowledge that comes from the enquiry into Nature. He stirreth up no evil for the citizens nor gives himself to unjust acts, but surveys the ageless order of immortal Nature, of what it is composed and how and why. In the heart of such as he the study of base acts can find no lodging.")

That Euripides should have felt constrained to proclaim the political innocence of the scientist is a precious light on the temper of his time. Anaxagoras was banished from Athens for publicly teaching his scientific views.

When we turn from physics to medicine we are struck by an equal devotion to the task of observation of phenomena. Against the passage we have quoted from Lucretius may be set the following description of the practice and achievement of the Hippocratic doctors:

"Greek medicine accomplished prodigies in the observation and classification of pathological symptoms. All the senses were called into service for this task, and that in a degree far beyond what is done to-day. The Hippocratic doctor observed the face of the sick man, its form, colour, and expression; also the different parts, the eyes, ears, nose, and tongue. He took note of the way in which the sick man held himself in the bed, and the part of the bed in which he lay, whether the top or the bottom; what he was doing with his hands, whether they were still or agitated as if in pain, as if the patient was trying to catch flies or scratch the wall. The skin, the nails, the hair were observed, the form and colour of the body, the state of strength, the appetite, shiverings, tremblings, also the urine, stools, expectorations, and blood. An ear was put against the wall of the chest, and the doctor heard a kind of gurgling—the rattling of the cavities—or again a kind of crepitation like that produced by a leather belt: the rubbing of the pleura attacked by a dry inflammation. Or else he shook the sick man and heard the ripple of the pleural effusion.

"By means of touch he noted the temperature of the patient, his pulse, the resistance to pressure offered by certain parts of the body, the situation, size, shape, consistence, and sensitivity of tumours, etc.

"But smell and taste were also put at the service of the examination. 'With feverish patients the nose furnishes many valuable indications, for the smells are very different from one another,' says the Hippocratic work on *Predictions*. And the Greek doctor did not shrink even from tasting the excreta.

"What could not be learned in this way was sought to be supplied by interrogating the patient: the onset of the disease, the subjective state of the invalid, his sleep and dreams, his hunger and thirst, his pains, his itchings, and other complaints.

"Without exaggeration it can be said that the Greek doctor allowed none of the pathological symptoms which can be perceived by the aid of the five senses to escape him."[3]

But, as has already been said, the Greek doctor was able to make an advance on the scientific method of the physicist. Having his material under his control, he avoided hypotheses (in the sense in which Newton used the word when he said *Hypotheses non fingo*) as much as possible, endeavouring always to submit his opinions to the test of observation. In the treatise entitled *Precepts* this point is discussed:

"One must attend in medicine not primarily to plausible theories, but to experience combined with reason. For a theory is a composite memory of things apprehended by sense-perception. For the sense-perception, coming first in experience and conveying to the intellect the things subjected to it, is clearly imaged, and the intellect, receiving these things many times, noting the occasion, the time and the manner, stores them up in itself and remembers. Now I approve of theorizing, if its foundations are laid in events, and its conclusions deduced in accordance with phenomena. . . . But if it begins, not from a clear impression, but from a plausible fiction, it often induces a grievous and troublesome condition. All who follow this method are lost in a blind alley. . . . Conclusions which are merely verbal cannot bear fruit; only those do which are based on demonstrated fact. For affirmation and talk are deceptive and treacherous. Wherefore one must hold fast to facts in generalizations also, and occupy oneself with facts persistently, if one is to acquire that ready and infallible habit which we call 'the art of Medicine.' "

This particular passage, being largely couched in technical Epicurean phraseology, must be dated in the third century B.C. But that it represents a tradition already two hundred years old in the medical schools is proved by the fifth century treatise *On Ancient Medicine*. In this treatise a vigorous protest is made against the attempt to base the science of medicine on the postulates or hypotheses of Empedoclean cosmology. The physical philosophers are bidden to keep their postulates for dealing with insoluble mysteries, "for example, things in the sky or under the ground." There they are in place, "for there is no test the application of which would give confirmation." But in medicine they are not in place, "for medicine has all its material under its control." This careful discussion of the place of hypothesis in the investigation of nature is one of the landmarks in the history of ancient science, and was not without its effect on modern science, the work *On Ancient Medicine* being much studied and pondered in the sixteenth, seventeenth, and eighteenth centuries of our own era.

If the nature of the material on which they worked brought the doctors in Ionia nearer than the physicists to the conception of modern science, it is possible also that the necessity of frequent and intimate contact with men who, owing to their sufferings, were most likely to be a prey to superstitious fears prompted them to greater efforts towards the rationalizing of the popular outlook. Be that as it may, we have no better example of the propaganda against superstition that characterized this epoch than the Hippocratic writing called *The Sacred Disease*:

"I am about to discuss the disease called Sacred (the disease was epilepsy). It is not, in my opinion, any more divine or more sacred than other diseases, but has a natural cause, and its supposed divine origin is due to men's inexperience, and to their wonder at its peculiar character. . . . But if it is to be considered divine just because it is wonderful, there will not be one sacred disease but many, for I will show that other diseases are no less wonderful and portentous, and yet nobody considers them sacred."

The irony of the passage is obvious, but equally obvious is its good-mannered suavity. It is as if the progress of enlightenment had advanced so far that the writer feels that the obscurantists are already despised and the ignorant can easily be rescued. This at least is the picture of society that seems to emerge for us as we continue the perusal of his treatise:

"My own view is that those who first attributed a sacred character to this malady were like the magicians, purifiers, charlatans, and quacks of our own day, men who claim great piety and superior knowledge. Being at a loss, and having no treatment which would help, they concealed and sheltered themselves behind superstition, and called this malady sacred, in order that their utter ignorance might not be exposed. . . .

"But perhaps what they profess is not true, the fact being that men in need of a livelihood contrive and devise many fictions of all sorts, about this disease among other things, putting the blame for each form of the affection upon a particular god. If the patient imitate a goat, if he roar, if the convulsion is in his right side, they say that the Mother of the Gods is to blame. If he utter a loud and piercing cry, they see a resemblance to a horse and blame Poseidon!

"But this disease is in my opinion no more divine than any other; it has the same nature as other diseases, and its own specific cause. . . .

"This disease styled sacred comes from the same causes as others, from the things that come to and go from the body, from cold, sun, and from the changing restlessness of the winds. These things are divine. So that there is no need to put the disease in a special class and to consider it more divine than others; they are all divine and all human. Each has a nature and power of its own; none is hopeless or incapable of treatment."

The humanity of this writing is no less remarkable than its scientific spirit. This was the epoch that has bequeathed to us the composite image of the Hippocratic physician, devoted equally to the patient investigation of nature and the patient service of humanity; the healer of mind and body, with his gospel of hope that the ills of men are not supernatural punishments, but natural afflictions which knowledge in time may alleviate. They tried not to hold out false hopes. "Art is long, life is short," they repeated, enforcing the truth of Xenophanes' words, "The gods have not revealed everything to men from the beginning, but men by searching in time find out better." Meantime the search and the service were felt to be the salt of life. To one who understands, knowledge of nature and love of humanity are not two things but one. Ἢν γὰρ παρῇ φιλανθρωπίη, πάρεστι καὶ φιλοτεχνίη. (Where the love of mankind is, there is also the love of the Art.)[4]

[1] Lucretius, De Rerum Natura, i, 265–328. Translation by H. A. J. Munro.

[2] Nauck, T. G. F., Euripides, 910.

[3] Translated from H. Sigerist, Introduction à la Médecine, 1932, pp. 110 ff. (English edition, Man and Medicine, London: George Allen & Unwin Ltd.)

[4] Precepts, chap. vi. Translations from the Hippocratic writings are taken, with occasional alterations, from the version of W. H. S. Jones in the Loeb Library, Heinemann.

CHAPTER SEVEN

PROMETHEUS BOUND

THE CLASH BETWEEN SCIENCE AND
THE CITY-STATE

The meaning of the Prometheus *of Aeschylus. The banishment
of Anaxagoras. The culture of the oligarchy as seen in
Theognis and Pindar.*

In the Athens of the middle of the fifth century the great
ideals of *Philanthropia* and *Philotechnia*, love of mankind and
love of science in its application to society, were made the
theme of a major work of art. In a setting worthy of such
high debate, the theatre of Dionysus itself, the problem of
accommodating them to the contemporary structure of
society was discussed. The great drama of Aeschylus, the
name of which we have taken as title for this chapter, unfolds
how the supreme god Zeus, the symbol of authority in the
universe and in society, has declared war upon the titan
Prometheus for his love of mankind. This love Prometheus
has manifested by stealing from heaven the gift of fire, and
teaching men all the arts of life. Zeus sends the god of fire
together with Might and Violence to punish the philan-
thropic rebel.

MIGHT (to Hephaestus, god of fire):

"To Earth's far-distant confines we are come,
The tract of Scythia, waste untrod by man.
    And now, Hephaestus, thou must mind the task
Ordained thee by the Father—to enchain

This malefactor on yon mountain crags
In indissoluble bands of adamant.
Thy flower, *fount of the arts*, the light of fire,
He stole and gave to mortals. Such the sin
For which he must make recompense to heaven,
And so be taught to accept the tyranny
Of Zeus, and check his *charity to man*.[1]

That Might and Violence should be the appointed instruments of the will of Zeus is notable; while the claim that it is for his philanthropy that Prometheus must be punished is stressed again and again throughout the play. And the theme that this philanthropy is identical with the creation of applied science is expanded to great compass in the central speeches of Prometheus (l. 436 to l. 506), ending in the proud boast:

"In these few words learn briefly my whole tale:
Prometheus founded all the arts of man."

Furthermore, the peculiar prominence given by Prometheus, in his recital of his achievements, to the invention of medicine is an indication of the relevance of the whole treatment of the problem to the state of science in Aeschylus' own day:

"Nay, hear the rest and thou wilt marvel more,
What cunning arts and artifices I planned.
Of all the greatest, if a man fell sick,
There was no remedy, nor shredded herb
Nor draught to drink nor ointment, and in default
Of physic their flesh withered, until I
Revealed the blends of gentle medicines
Wherewith they arm themselves against disease."

No less emphatic is the insistence that Prometheus, by promoting the welfare of mankind through the application of science, is in the eyes of the symbol of authority a malefactor. He is so called expressly. His foil is the hinge-backed lackey of Zeus, Oceanus, symbol of political submissiveness. ("Save thyself, as thou know'st how," is Prometheus' bitter counsel to him.) His fellow-victim is Typho, the symbol of popular revolt. It would seem, therefore, clear that what Aeschylus has dramatized in the *Prometheus* is the political problem of adjusting contemporary institutions to meet the great upheaval of the old ways of life represented by the Ionian enlightenment. I accept the conclusions of Professor George Thomson[2] that the trilology of the *Prometheia* was the last work of the poet, and was therefore composed between 458 and 456; that the *Prometheus Bound* was the first play of the three; and that in the end Aeschylus, who was a moderate democrat, had found a reconciliation between the protagonists of the drama. But since my own interpretation contains, so far as I can judge, an element of originality, I shall seek to justify it by a brief consideration of the historical setting of the play.

It is the merit of Whittaker, in his *Priests, Philosophers and Prophets*,[3] to have stressed the importance of the deliberately constructed element in the "revealed" religions of Zoroastrianism, Judaism, and Christianity. He would classify religions, according to the degree of their development, as Natural, More or less organized, and Revealed, the latter belonging to the most self-conscious stage and being properly described as constructed. Accepting this classification, our purpose must be to estimate the constructed element in the "more or less organized" religion of Athens at this period. This is essential to our enquiry. Aeschylus was concerned not only with personal religion, but with the organization of public religion in the State cult. His purpose in the *Prometheia*, as I understand it, was to offer to the Athenian public a conception of Zeus that would not be incompatible with the Ionian enlightenment.

In the ancient civilizations of the Near East an ethical monotheism, such as the more religious among the Greek philosophers also inclined to teach, had been the common possession of the Babylonian and Egyptian priesthoods at least since the middle of the second millennium. But this monotheistic religion of the ancient priesthoods was an esoteric doctrine; the mass of the people accepted the polytheistic myths and no effort was made to enlighten them. Or rather the general temper of these ancient societies was against such attempts at enlightenment, and such attempts as were made were defeated. Thus, the truth about the religious reforms of Akhnaton, early in the fourteenth century B.C., would seem to be, not that he introduced for the first time the conception of monotheism, but that he introduced it to the people. His effort was abortive. As Whittaker puts it: "The priests won in the end. The old ceremonial was restored, with the offerings by which it was maintained; and not only did it continue after the destruction of the simpler worship initiated by the 'heretic king,' but it encroached more and more on civic life, so that henceforth the fate of Egypt was slow decay under its hierarchic petrification."

It was the well-founded opinion of Burnet[4] that there was a period, say the seventh to the fifth centuries, when a similar fate threatened Greek society. "It looked as if Greek religion were about to enter on the same stage as that already reached by the religions of the East; and, but for the rise of science, it is hard to see what could have checked this tendency. The existence of the scientific schools saved Greece." This pregnant analysis is defective only in the important sense that Burnet shows, perhaps, an insufficient appreciation of the fact that science has little chance of ultimate victory over priestly opposition unless it should succeed in embodying itself in the political institutions of the state. The struggle between science and obscurantism is ultimately a political one. Obscurantism remained enthroned in the seat of political power in Athens and in Greece, and the "salvation" of which Burnet speaks was temporary. Byzantinism was not the ultimate outcome of a Greece that had been "saved by the scientific schools." Anna Comnena did not thumb the Ionian physicists, wide as her reading was, but the *Dialogues* of Plato and the *Rhetoric* of Aristotle.[5] And the seeds of Byzantinism were already sown, as we shall see, in the fourth century.

But we must now return to Aeschylus and the Athens of the fifth century. *Pari passu* with the scientific movement in Ionia, and not unconnected with it in the case of some of the leaders of thought, had developed a tendency to purify the traditional polytheism by a movement towards ethical monotheism. Xenophanes and Heracleitus are conspicuous examples of this tendency, nor was their younger contemporary, Aeschylus, untouched by it. In his case the particular form the tendency took was to emphasize and exalt the importance of Zeus in the Olympian pantheon. His genius was both theological and dramatic. And the bringing into being of the democratic Athens of the fifth century, with its novel institutions, involved politico-religious questions of great scope and complexity, with the solution of which Aeschylus was preoccupied throughout his life.

In the old days of the oligarchy the religious needs of the

people were not provided for by the centralized state. Religion was in the control of the noble families, and the commoners, like the slaves, were admitted to participate in the family cults—at discretion. It was precisely this aristo-cratic structure of Athenian society in its politico-religious aspect that prevented the democratic constitution of Solon from coming into effect. The essential reform of Cleisthenes, which effectively brought democracy into operation, was the break up of the old aristocratic organization of religion by shattering the old clan system of the phratries, replacing it by new units, the demes, organized on a territorial basis, and democratizing religion by giving every citizen a share in the state cult by virtue of his citizenship.⁶ The victory of the democracy received concrete expression in the fact that republican officials, elected or appointed by lot, took over the administration of the state cult, and questions of religious policy were henceforth to be determined by the vote of the assembly of the people. The incompleteness of the victory, and the tenacity of the nobles, were illustrated by the survival of the old practice that the interpreters of the sacral law—a vague function, which, like that exercised by the augurs in Rome, might at critical moments assume decisive importance —should always be members of the nobility. Control of the state religion, therefore, was one of the spoils of office in the desperate class-warfare of antiquity.

From this brief sketch of the relation between religion and politics in Athens it follows that if innovations were attempted in the traditional beliefs opposition might be expected from either, or both, parties in the state. In the ancient Athenian form of democracy, as in the modern British variety, there were strong survivals of oligarchy. Government tended to remain effectively in the control of a limited number of families, and the butcher, the baker, and the candlestick maker, if they pushed themselves into positions of prominence and responsibility, were apt to find that they were generally considered to have got out of their proper place. Under a democratic political exterior the oligarchy governed unobstrusively. In oligarchic circles, although individuals might be genuinely religious or genuinely superstitious, the state religion tended to be regarded with more or less open cynicism as a political device for the maintenance of some degree of "stability" in the state.

In such circles the speculations of Ionian physicists would produce little opposition in themselves. They might be accepted as true or condemned as false, but in themselves they were not dangerous. The danger began and the opposition was aroused when they seemed to be getting a hold upon the people and endangering the institution of the state cult. A society not held together by the bond of justice, expressed in an equitable distribution of wealth, cannot afford to relax any other bond that may serve to hold it together. Of these the state cults were both the most effective and the most unobtrusive.

At the same time, if it were necessary to raise the alarm of a threat to religion, the oligarchy was sure of a wide support from among the people. This arose partly from such affection as the people might feel for their traditional institutions, and partly from the solid advantages which the democracy enjoyed by virtue of their increased participation in the control of the cults. Certain feasts, Nilsson reminds us, were celebrated on a very large scale, the state entertaining the citizens, and the sums expended were by no means small. "The great festivals were the only opportunities which many of the people had of enjoying roast meat." The Dionysiac festivals, the Festival of Pitchers, the Panathenaea, were such occasions; and to the material good things were

junction of kt

added the delights of music and literature, and the parade before the numerous visitors who thronged the city at these times of the glory and the greatness of Athens. "It is no wonder," Nilsson concludes, "that the Athenian citizens clung to the religion which gave them so many privileges, and that they maintained the state cult and religious tradition. When the age of enlightenment began to direct its unaccommodating intellectual criticism even against cults and gods, religious persecutions began." But such persecutions were not, as he implies, exclusively the work of the democracy. For this correction of his view we hope to supply proof in the sequel.

About twenty-five years after the production of the *Prometheus* of Aeschylus we have evidence, in the *Clouds* of the comic poet Aristophanes, that the problem created by the new ideas of the Ionian philosophers had not yet ceased to trouble the Athenian public. But it is in between the date of these two plays that the most striking factual, as apart from literary, proof of the depth of the unrest is afforded by the circumstance of the expulsion of the philosopher Anaxagoras from Athens. Anaxagoras was an ideal embodiment of the spirit of Ionian science. A native of Clazomenae, and a man of property and position, he was entitled, had he cared for it, to look forward to a political career in his own country. But, we are told, he surrendered both property and politics (in the narrow sense) lest they should interfere with his quest for a knowledge of the nature of things. He settled in Athens, where he had the countenance of Pericles and the friendship of Euripides; but there he found, as we have pointed out in our Introduction that Haeckel also found, that to be an uncompromising public champion of the conclusions of science is to be a politician, in the widest and noblest sense. In Athens he came to exercise great influence not only owing to his attainments in astronomy and mathematics, but still more owing to "the ascetic dignity of his nature, and his superiority to ordinary weaknesses." These are the words of William Wallace, a true admirer of Anaxagoras, but not, I think, a sure guide as to the role of the democracy in his impeachment.

"His observations of the celestial bodies," writes Wallace, "led him to form new theories of the universal order, and brought him into collision with the popular faith which found the objects of its worship in the heavens. The dominant polytheism and the ignorance of the multitude could not tolerate such explanation; and the enemies of Pericles used the superstitions of their countrymen as a means of attacking the ideas of that statesman in the person of his friend."[7]

There is much that is confused in this. We are told that the offence of Anaxagoras was against the popular faith, the dominant polytheism, and the ignorance of the multitude. But we are also told that the attack was a disguised political manœuvre. These two explanations do not fit together. And there is another difficulty. The popular worship in the Athens of the time was not directed in any strength towards the heavenly bodies. When the Athenians thought of Apollo, they thought of the god who presided over the oracle of Delphi, not of the sun. Their cult of the sun was, at this date, very unimportant. In fact there was nothing in the teaching of Anaxagoras on the heavenly bodies or on meteoric phenomena calculated in itself to raise a popular clamour for his impeachment. And the report of Plutarch is that at a time when Pericles was being indirectly attacked in the persons both of the sculptor Pheidias, and of his mistress Aspasia, then also the oracle-monger Diopeithes took occasion to

75

stir up further feeling against the harassed statesman by bringing in a motion before the people, aimed at his friend Anaxagoras. The impeachment was in vague terms. It was directed against all those "who do not practice the state religion or who give lessons on celestial phenomena." It is an incorrect interpretation, in the opinion of the present writer, to regard such a motion before the assembly as proof of an outbreak of uncontrollable resentment on the part of the ignorant mob. What it proves is something quite different, namely the existence of a habit of exploiting the religious prejudices of the people for political ends.

Those who repeat the phrase that the opposition to Ionian science arose from the ignorance of the masses, and who thus imply that Ionian science was welcomed by the classes, create a wholly erroneous view of the cultural history of this vital period. We have only to look at the writings of the spokesmen of the aristocracy to perceive its falsity. These views are generally sought in the remains of Theognis and Pindar. We could want no better evidence. Theognis makes it abundantly clear that in his opinion religion has one function, to preserve the aristocratic organization of society. He was passionately of the opinion, to adopt the phraseology of Plutarch's friend Florus, that things ought to be divided up by geometrical proportion and not by arithmetic; and if God was not going to busy Himself with geometry in this way, it is made quite clear that, in the opinion of the poet, He was not doing His duty. Such a man is the natural enemy of ideas, in so far as ideas involve any threat to the established order of things. A poet always forceful and sometimes deeply moving in a tender vein of sentiment—the six lines in which he expresses his love for his native Megara are a more exquisite poem even than Du Bellay's *Heureux qui, comme Ulysse, a fait un beau voyage*—he shocks by his bitter hatred of any class but his own and his identification of virtue with ownership of land. One might measure the moral progress of humanity in the space of two thousand five hundred years by the contrast between the attitudes of Theognis and Tolstoy to the peasantry.

There is, unhappily, only too much in common between the crabbed philosophy of Theognis and the ideas that dominate the outlook of the Theban poet, Pindar. Pindar was the almost exact contemporary of Aeschylus, and he spent his life in the service of the aristocracy of the Greek world, as Aeschylus did in that of the democracy of Athens. The choral lyric was the art form of the Dorian aristocracy; the drama was the expression of Athenian democracy. The victory odes of Pindar were commissioned and paid for by the tyrants or noble families throughout Greece, and performed at functions organized by them. The dramas of Aeschylus were submitted, in competition with the works of other poets, to a public official of the demos; accepted by him; produced at the expense of the state, and at a state function at which the attendance of the whole people was expected and encouraged. A performance in the theatre of Dionysus was as much an expression of the democratic life of the Athenian people as a meeting of the Assembly. The performance of a Pindaric ode, the expenses of which were born by the wealthy victor—Psaumis of Camarina, or Hagesias of Syracuse, or Xenocrates of Acragas, or Megacles of Athens, or Chromius of Aetna, or Herodotus of Thebes—was a festival of the aristocracy, an expression of the enormous power still in the hands of the landed families of the Greek world. In the victory odes of Pindar, therefore, we shall find the reflection of the oligarchic view of life.

77

It is not too much to say that this view is wholly incompatible with the spirit of the Ionian enlightenment. In the first place the normal assumption is that any aristocratic family is of divine origin, being descended a few generations back (no doubt about the time the foundation of the family fortune was laid) from some god or demi-god who engendered with a mortal woman.

Closely connected with this theory of the divine origin of the noble families is the belief in the hereditary character of distinguished virtue of any kind. Our modern scholars treat this belief with too much respect, as if Pindar was entitled to an opinion on the subject. "The modern theory of the hereditary transmission of qualities, which in this century is being worked out in so many directions, would have found a warm advocate in Pindar. He believed in the derivation of excellences, physical and moral, from the ancient heroes, to whom such families traced their descent; and he disdained the doctrine that excellences might be acquired."[8] So wrote the late J. B. Bury. Pindar *believed* in the derivation of excellences, physical and moral, from the *ancient heroes, to whom such families traced their descent.* This is to take too simple a view. For, as Bury himself pointed out, "the doctrine might be perverted by an upholder of aristocracies and monarchies in support of his political prejudices."

Naturally, in this society of semi-divine beings, life did not proceed on the ordinary hum-drum level. At important crises it was guided by oracles and sustained by miracles. And though Pindar, we are asked to believe, was a biologist with an important opinion on problems which have caused some difficulty to modern enquirers, he had also at command a source of information more reliable and much less burdensome than the toilsome researches of the poor Hippocratic doctors. This was the Pythian Apollo, who, Pindar assures us, "knows the end supreme of all things, and all the ways that lead thereto; the number of the leaves that the earth putteth forth in the spring; the number of the sands that in the sea and the rivers are driven before the waves and the rushing winds; that which is to be and whence it is to come." And the veracity of the god was equal to his omniscience. Apollo, Pindar assures us, "can have nothing to do with falsehood." And on these matters Pindar was likely to be well informed. His connexion with the Delphic priesthood was intimate. He enjoyed, indeed, a sort of perpetual endowment secured on the prosperity of the oracle. Pausanias tells us[9] that the Pythia, the oracular priestess of Apollo, bade the Delphians give Pindar an equal share in all the first-fruits they offered to Apollo, and that the poet's posterity continued to enjoy the privilege long after his death.

Pindar, therefore, in spite of his scientific tastes, preferred sources of information more rapid, secure, and, it may be added, more reliable in the political character of the truth supplied, than those available to the Ionian physicists. Not unnaturally he despised them, and did not hesitate to say so. "The Natural Philosophers reap an ineffectual harvest from their wisdom"[10]—an ambiguous phrase from which we shall spare to squeeze any other meaning than his obvious antipathy to their views.

It will not surprise anybody familiar with a complex of beliefs such as Pindar's to find that his certainties embraced also the world beyond the grave. He believed in the after-life and was informed with a reasonable degree of precision on the different lots that there awaited the just and the unjust. His eschatological lessons had also been learned from Apollo. "We may be sure," writes the historian of the

Delphic Oracle, "that Pindar, whom the Oracle bade have an equal share of the first-fruits with Apollo himself, was but voicing his sentiments when, with almost scriptural clearness, he contrasts the future life of the virtuous and the wicked. 'The good, having the sun shining for evermore, share among the honoured gods a life that knoweth no tears, where around the Isles of the Blest the ocean-breezes blow, and there is a blaze of golden flowers.' But 'the lawless spirits, whose sins committed in this realm of Zeus are judged by one that passeth sentence stern and inevitable,' are punished immediately after death" (*Olympian*, ii, 57–80).[11] With Pindar, as with Theognis, it should be remembered the "good" and the "lawless" are political rather than moral terms. As that excellent editor, Basil Gildersleeve, remarked, Pindar's belief in the next world "is of a piece with the aristocratic character of his mind, the continuation of the proper distinction between Good and Bad, in the Doric sense."

"Under every form of government," says Pindar in his second *Pythian Ode*, "a man of straightforward speech comes to the front, whether at the tyrant's court, or where the turbulent host, or where the wise, manage the state." His political terminology is worthy of note. By the government of the turbulent host he means democracy; by that of the wise he means oligarchy. Obviously this is a terminology in which no democrat could acquiesce, and there is evidence that Aeschylus was not content with it. It would be out of place here to pursue this enquiry into detail. But, if we accept the view of the editor quoted above, that "the detail of Pindar's odes produces an irresistible effect of opulence," and that "opulence is wealth that makes itself felt, that suggests, almost insultingly, a contrast, and that contrast is indigence"—then we must admit that the pervading temper of Pindar's work bears the closest resemblance to the Pride, or Hybris, which Aeschylus condemns in all his plays.

We can now sum the matter up. Throughout his dramatic career, so far as we can judge by the extant plays, Aeschylus was concerned always with the one public theme, the enterprise, so fateful for humanity, of securing the constitution of the Athenian democracy, the great experiment in government on which the eyes of the whole Greek world were turned. In his *Persae* he had sung the victory ode for the triumph of democracy over its Persian foe. In the *Seven Against Thebes* the question of the establishment of a state cult is heavy on his mind. The "gods that hold the city" (πολισσοῦχοι θεοί) dominate the play.

In the three parts of the trilogy of the *Oresteia*, and in the *Suppliants*, the preoccupation is plainly with the survivals of the older pre-city form of society and the new institutions of the city-state itself. The evolution of society is the poet's theme, and it is plain that in the main he is satisfied with the form it has taken in the moderate democracy of Athens.

What then remained for him to do? There was an aspect of the problem of democracy not yet discussed, the thorniest of all. Every advance of the democracy had been a victory for enlightenment won in the teeth of opposition. It had been a bitter struggle to wrest from the oligarchs a written code of law; Draco had yielded, but with what reluctance and ill-grace! The aristocratic monopoly of the control of religion had held up the establishment of democracy for the best part of a century after Solon framed his constitution. We may be sure that the proposal to refer religious questions, which had traditionally been settled by the aristocratic head of a clan, to the many-headed populace assembled in the Ecclesia would be one of those occasions on which, in Pindar's view, Zeus would have been well advised to launch a thunderbolt. To make democracy feasible the people had to be educated; they must be able to scratch a name on a potsherd, to decide whether or not to banish an aristocrat who threatened to become too powerful. "Trample on the empty-headed populace; goad them hard and let their yoke be heavy—that is the way to make them love their masters"—such had been the advice of Theognis. But now they are to gather in the Assembly and decide policy. They are to sit in the law courts and administer justice, and be paid a day's wage for doing so. "The city is still the city, but the people are changed," groaned Theognis when Megara was threatened with a similar popular revolt. "For the people before knew neither justice nor law, but they wrapped their stiff goat-skins about their ribs and stayed outside the city like deer; and now they are good, and the good are humbled. Who could see it and live?"[12] And, to make matters worse, through the length and breadth of Greece there began to appear men like Anaxagoras, who settled in their cities, or men like Protagoras, who travelled from city to city, who justified the new order of things, and undermined the views on which the old order had rested. We have seen of what offence Anaxagoras was guilty. Protagoras, for his part, taught that every man, in virtue of his humanity, was possessed of a sense of honour and of justice and was therefore capable of fulfilling the role of a citizen.[13] It was a charter of democratic rights. He taught that Man is the measure of all things, or, in other words, that he is free to alter his institutions to suit himself. This stripped the divine sanction from the *status quo*.

What was the attitude of a moderate democrat to be to such things? Aeschylus had been optimistic that in the Athens that had re-arisen triumphant after the Persian war stability had been reached. But the thing was a compromise.

[What Athens had got was, after all, a timocracy not a *after Persian war*
democracy; there were injustices enshrined in the constitution that were to bring the city to civil war again
before the end of the century. And was the City-State, in
its religious aspect, any better secured? Was it not, too, a
compromise, incapable of withstanding the attacks of the
enlightenment? Apollo was among the gods that held the
city; but Aeschylus had already voiced his doubts of the
trustworthiness of Apollo. And Zeus, the supreme god
Zeus? How was Aeschylus to reconcile the god of his
intimate devotion with Zeus to whom Theognis prayed to
destroy his class enemies, or the god with the thunderbolt
to whom Pindar looked to save Greece from democracy?

In his *Prometheia* Aeschylus thought out the problem of
the city-state again from the point of view of the conflict
between authority and enlightenment. In the first part of
the trilogy, the *Prometheus Bound*, which is all that we
possess, he was concerned to state the problem, not to give
his solution. On the one side he gives us the picture of
Zeus the tyrant; he is the blind, repressive Zeus of the
oligarchic reactionaries, painted without a redeeming
feature, as cruel, false, and selfish as he is powerful. Against
him he sets on the other hand the ideal figure of the enlightenment, the lover of mankind who comes with wisdom
in his gift. But it is clear that he withholds from him his
full approval. His Prometheus was rash, headstrong, obsti-
nate, unreasonable. What does this signify, if not that
reform, especially with such dangerous allies as the hundred-
headed Typho,

"Hissing forth terror from his horrid jaws,"

must learn to observe caution, to go slowly, to respect
authority? What solution, then, can ultimately be found,

83

what reconciliation between ignorant repression and rash reform? What is possible, except that authority should become instructed and humane, and reform wise and patient? Some such solution Aeschylus, we know, contrived. With the possible detail of his solution we are not concerned. What remains for our enquiry is the striking fact that in the Athens of the middle of the fifth century B.C. her most profoundly imaginative poet should have realized with such overwhelming conviction the political problem raised by the new knowledge. In essence his problem was the same as that raised by Tolstoy in his famous essay, *What is Religion?* "It seems to men natural that Government—which justifies its existence on the score of its care for the welfare of the people—must, to secure that welfare, wish to use only the means which can never do people any harm, and can only produce the most fruitful results. Government, however, has not only never taken upon itself this duty, but, on the contrary, has always and everywhere maintained with the greatest jealousy any false, effete religion prevalent at the period, and has in every way persecuted those who have tried to inform the people of the principles of true religion." But Aeschylus, of course, sees the problem in the light of his own convictions and in the terms of his own day, the brutal ignorance of the reaction with its ministers Might and Violence, the eager humanity of the enlightenment, and the danger of its association with the many-headed people.[14]

[1] Aeschylus, *Prometheus Bound*, 1-11. Translation by George Thomson, whose version is used also in the other quotations from this play.

[2] See the Introduction to Aeschylus, *Prometheus Bound*, by George Thomson, Cambridge, 1932.

[3] Thomas Whittaker, *Priests, Philosophers and Prophets*, A. and C. Black, 1911.

[4] Burnet, *Early Greek Philosophy*, 2nd ed., p. 87.

[5] See Anna Comnena, *Alexias*, I.

[6] Nilsson, *A History of Greek Religion*, Oxford, 1925.

[7] William Wallace, *Encyclopaedia Britannica* (9th ed.).

[8] *The Nemean Odes of Pindar*, edited by J. B. Bury, Macmillan, 1890, p. 38.

[9] Pausanias, ix, 23, 2.

[10] Τοὺς φυσιολογοῦντας ἔφη ἀτελῆ σοφίας δρέπειν καρπόν. See Donaldson's *Pindar*, Fragments 123, 124. Also Plato, *Theaet.* 173D; Plato, *Rep.* 457B; Clem. Alex., *Str.* 20, 707; Stobaeus, *Serm.* ccxi, p. 711.

[11] Rev. T. Dempsey, *The Delphic Oracle, Its Early History, Influence and Fall*, p. 149.

[12] The passages quoted from Theognis are 847-849 (George Thomson's version), and 53-58. Note the class-use of the word "good."

[13] Plato, *Protagoras*, chap. 9: "And Hermes said to Zeus, 'In what way shall I distribute the sense of honour and justice among men? Shall I distribute them as the arts are distributed? For, in the distribution of the arts, one man who is a doctor is worth many ordinary men, and so with other craftsmen. Am I to distribute the sense of justice and honour in this way among men, or am I to give it to all?' '*To all*,' said Zeus, '*all are to share in them. Otherwise cities would be impossible, that is, if only the few shared the understanding of justice and honour, as is the case with the arts.*'"

[14] As far as dates go, there would not appear to be any difficulty in connecting the *Prometheus* with the situation in Athens that resulted in the impeachment and trial of Anaxagoras. The probable date of the composition of the *Prometheia* is 458-456. Already in 450, according to the dating of Brunot and Mieli (*Histoire des Sciences Antiquité*: p. 1117), *Anaxagore, poursuivi, semble-t-il, pour ses opinions scientifiques, quitte Athènes*. His final expulsion came, probably, in 432. But this was only a crisis in a struggle between the nature of the *polis* and the claims of the enlightenment which had been gathering strength for generations. It should be remembered that Thales, Anaximander, and Pythagoras,

as well as Solon, were legislators. Unless the minds of these great men were so constructed that their different mental activities took place in water-tight compartments, they must, already in the sixth century, have pondered much on the bearing of the new view of the world on the question of the organization of the city-state. Aeschylus was handling an old theme. (For the political activities of the Ionian scientists, see F. Enriques et G. de Santillana, *Histoire de la Pensée Scientifique*, I, *Les Ioniens et La Nature des Choses*, Paris, 1936, p. 26, note.) Protagoras too was a legislator.

CHAPTER EIGHT

PLATO AND THE RELIGION OF THE CITY-STATE

Critias and the political view of the origin of religion. Isocrates and the political function of religion. Plato's religious legislation. Its incompatibility with Ionian science.

Plato was born in the year in which Anaxagoras is supposed to have died. In the interval which separated the two men the attitude of Athens to Ionian science had become more clearly defined and the antagonism had deepened. It was not only that Socrates had begun his powerful movement of revolt against Ionian materialism; the technique of government through religion was also better understood as well as the threat to this technique inherent in the spread of Ionian rationalism.

The political self-consciousness of Athens was a thing of very rapid growth. It corresponded to the equally rapid growth of Athenian democracy. "In less than one hundred and fifty years Athens passed from the domination of the Eupatrids to the full expansion of the democratic regime."[1] The emancipation of the people from the political control of the nobles had not been effected without a challenge to the religion of the nobility, and this challenge sharpened in the nobility the understanding of the political function of religion. Two familiar texts reveal this understanding. They are too important to the argument to be omitted here.

87

We shall first consider a fragment from a drama by the oligarch Critias, the disciple of Socrates and relative of Plato, in which he expounds the theory of the political origin of religion very commonly held in the eighteenth century of our own era. I quote Whittaker's version (*op. cit.*, p. 77):

"There was a time when the life of men was unordered and brutish and subjected to main force; when there was no reward for the good and no punishment came to the bad. And then, I think, men appointed laws as chastisers, that justice should be ruler and keep wanton insolence in bondage: and if one transgressed, he was punished. Thereafter, when the laws hindered indeed wrongful works done by open violence, but men continued to do them by stealth, some shrewd and wise-thoughted man found an object of awe for mortals, that there might be some object of dread to the wicked even if they do or say or think anything in secret. Whence he brought in the divinity (τὸ θεῖον), telling them that there is a Deity (ὡς ἔστι δαίμων), vigorous with imperishable life, hearing and seeing with the mind, with sure thought attending to these things, and clothed with a divine nature, who will hear all that is said among mortals and will have power to see all that is done. And if in silence thou plan a wicked deed, this shall not escape the gods: for in them is careful thought. By this discourse he introduced the most welcome of teachings, hiding the truth with a false story (ψευδεῖ καλύψας τὴν ἀλήθειαν λόγῳ). And there, where he could most astound the senses of men by saying that the gods dwelt, there he placed them: in the vault of heaven above, whence, he knew, are the terrors that descend upon mortals and the benefits that help their toilsome life. There he saw that the lightnings were, and the dire strokes of the thunder, and the star-eyed body of the sky, the fair-wrought broidery of Time, the wise artist; whence rises the glowing mass of the day-star and moist showers are poured down to earth. Such lines of fear he set around men, and fairly constituted the Deity by his fiction and in a fitting place, and quelled lawlessness with laws. . . . Thus, in my opinion, some one first persuaded mortals to think that there is a race of deities."

As a contribution to the philosophical understanding of religion the passage is immature. Critias was wrong in supposing (if indeed he did suppose; it is not fair to judge a man by an isolated fragment of a dramatic composition) that in disclosing the political function of religion, he had discovered its genesis. But that such a clear and cynical analysis of the political function of religion should have been made, and published, at this time is significant of the preoccupation of statesmen with such problems. The false religion is the work of a law-giver, "a shrewd and wise-thoughted man." In the opinion of another public man of the time, the rhetorician and educationist, Isocrates, the political function of religion could be as well, or better, discharged by a degraded polytheism as by the refined invention of an invisible god in the sky. In his amusing composition *Busiris* he thus interprets for his Athenian public the intentions of the religious legislator of the Egyptians:

"The pious practices which he introduced were many and various; for he established by law that they should reverence and honour animals that are despised among us, not because he was under any misapprehension as to the power of these creatures, but for two other reasons. The first was that he thought it proper to accustom the mob to obeying any commands that were given to them by their superiors; the second, that he wished to test, by their attention to these public observances, the sentiments his subjects might entertain on matters more difficult to observe. For he thought that men who despised these little observances might very well also feel contempt for more important things, while he could rely on those who displayed their piety to be equally law-abiding in every other particular."

The tone is light, but the passage is none the less revealing on that account. It is the kind of evidence that most helps one who endeavours to recreate the temper of a distant society. It assures him that he is not introducing into his period a range of ideas wholly foreign to it. That these ideas were not foreign to fourth-century Athens a consideration of Plato will make clear. There are moments when one could wish that his treatment were equally light-hearted.

The view has been expressed that "philosophy is perhaps less influenced by outward circumstances than most branches of human thought and literature." This would hardly seem to be true of the one who to many is the philosopher *par excellence*, Plato. In his famous Seventh Epistle he himself tells of the connexion between his own philosophy and the politics of the day:

"The more I thought about the sort of men who were active in politics, the more I examined laws and customs, and the more I advanced in years, the harder it appeared to me to govern correctly. For one thing, nothing could be done without friends and loyal companions, and such men were not easy to find ready to hand, since our city was no longer administered according to the standards and practices of our fathers. Neither could such men be created afresh with any facility. What is more, the written laws and customs were being corrupted at an astounding rate. The result was that I, who had been full of eagerness for a public career, as I gazed upon the whirlpool of public life and saw the incessant movement of shifting currents, at last became dizzy; and, while I did not cease to consider means of improving the situation and indeed reforming the whole constitution, yet, in regard to action I kept waiting for favourable moments, and finally saw clearly in regard to all States now existing that without exception their system of government is bad. Their constitutions are almost beyond redemption except through some miraculous plan assisted by good luck. Hence I was forced to the conclusion that only the true philosophy can enable us to discern in all cases what is good for communities and individuals: and that accordingly the human race will not see better days until either the stock of those who rightly and genuinely follow philosophy acquire political power, or else the class who have political control be lead by some dispensation of providence to become real philosophers."

Such were the outward circumstances that determined that the great work of Plato's first period should be the ten books of the *Republic* and the great work of his old age should be the twelve books of the *Laws*. The whole philosophy of Plato was a political philosophy, and the controlling purpose of his long life, which gathered clarity as he proceeded with his task, was the construction of a system of belief and a system of education which, being imposed by the governing authority, would guarantee the well-being of the State. Preoccupation with the *polis* was as definitely the mainspring of the Platonic movement as preoccupation with nature had been the mainspring of the Ionian movement.

It is the startling opinion of A. E. Taylor that it was the heart of Plato's thought that "there can be no difference in spirit between the laws of public and of private morality." "Whoever holds," he continues, "that what would be 'morally' reprehensible for the individual person may be 'politically' admirable when done by the official representatives of the State, has broken with the whole view of the reasons for civic loyalty and political subjection characteristic of both Plato and Aristotle."[2] But one would have thought that Plato's own words put it beyond question that the melancholy discovery of the difference in relation to Truth between the individual and the State was the keystone of his political philosophy. Let us quote:

"Truth should be highly valued; if, as we were saying, a lie is useless to the gods, and useful only as a medicine to men, then the use of such medicines should be restricted to physicians; private individuals have no business with them."

"Certainly not."

"Then if any one at all is to have the privilege of lying, the rulers of the State should be the persons; and they, in their dealings either with enemies or with their own citizens, may be allowed to lie for the public good. But nobody else should meddle with anything of the kind; and although the rulers have this privilege, for a private man to lie to them in return is to be deemed a more heinous fault than for the patient or the pupil of a gymnasium not to speak truth about his own bodily illnesses to the physician or to the trainer, or for a sailor not to tell the captain what is happening about the ship and the rest of the crew, and how things are going with himself or his fellow sailors."

"Most true."

"If, then, the ruler catches anybody beside himself lying in the State,

Any of the craftsmen, whether he be priest or physician or carpenter

(*Od.* XVII, 383),

he will punish him for introducing a practice which is equally subversive and destructive of ship or State."

"Most certainly, if our idea of the State is ever carried out."

Republic, iii, 389.

Now one may like or dislike this, defend or attack it, but how can one, in face of it, maintain that Plato's view was that there should be no difference in spirit between the laws of public and private morality? Except, indeed, in this sense, that it was Plato's notion that the governmental "lie" should be so skilfully adapted to its purpose, and so thoroughly inculcated by training, that it should become second nature, and that there should be no possibility that the subjects should ever in thought or act question the truth of the governors. To them it should appear that truth reigned throughout the State.

Plato's intention was, of course, that the governmental lie should be a medicinal doctrine that should ensure the health of the individual and of society. But why was it that he feared the truth? On the title-page of this book I have printed the proud words of Epicurus, who carried on the tradition of Ionian science. "The study of nature turns out a type of man not prone to boasting or words nor to the display of that culture so desired by the many, but spirited and self-sufficient, basing his pride on his personal qualities not on external goods." This type of man, and this type of education, had found favour with the leaders of the enlightenment and of democracy, who had believed that it was the common prerogative of all men to be capable of understanding and appreciating justice and therefore capable of full participation in the life of the State. Such, for instance, had been the teaching of the Sophist Protagoras, and such, we shall see, was the Epicurean view. Plato was incapable of this belief. He had so little faith in human nature that democracy was to him a mere chimera. It was to banish for ever the possibility of popular revolts and to establish a class-divided society on a secure basis that he sought to call in the aid of the governmental lie, and so to stamp it upon the soul of the people that they should be for ever incapable of questioning its truth. Who with any sense of the human tragedy of the twenty-three centuries that separate us from Plato can read his proposals without a sense of horror? I quote again from the *Republic*:

"How then may we devise one of those needful falsehoods of which we lately spoke—just one royal lie which may deceive the rulers, if that be possible, and at any rate the rest of the city?"

"What sort of lie?"

"Nothing new; only an old Phoenician tale of what has often occurred before now in other places, as the poets say, and have made the world believe, though not in our time, and I do not know whether such a thing could ever happen again, or that people could now be made to believe it if it did."

"How your words seem to hesitate on your lips!"

"You will not wonder at my hesitation when you have heard."

"Speak and fear not."

"Well then I will speak, although I really know not how to look you in the face, or in what words to utter the audacious fiction, which I propose to communicate gradually, first to the rulers, then to the soldiers, and lastly to the people. They are to be told that their youth was a dream, and the education and training which they received from us, an appearance only; in reality during all that time they were being formed and fed in the womb of the earth, where they themselves and their arms and appurtenances were manufactured; when they were completed, the earth, their mother, sent them up; and so, their country being their mother and their nurse, they are bound to advise for her good, and to defend her against attacks, and her citizens they are to regard as children of earth and their own brothers."

"You had good reason to be ashamed of the lie you were going to tell."

"True, but there is more coming; I have only told you half. Citizens, we shall say to them in our tale, you are brothers, yet God has framed you differently. Some of you have the power of command, and in the composition of these he has mingled gold, wherefore also they have the greatest honour; others he has made of silver, to be auxiliaries; others again who are to be husbandmen and craftsmen he has composed of brass and iron; and the species will generally be preserved in the children. But as all are of the same original stock, a golden parent will sometimes have a silver son, or a silver parent a golden son. And God proclaims as a first principle to the rulers, and above all else, that there is nothing which they should so anxiously consider, or of which they are to be such good guardians, as of the purity of the race. They should observe what elements mingle in their offspring; for if the son of a golden or silver father has an admixture of brass or iron, then nature orders a transposition of ranks; and the eye of the ruler must not be pitiful towards the child because he has to descend in the scale and become a husbandman or artisan, just as there may be sons of artisans who having an admixture of gold or silver in them are raised to honour, and become guardians or auxiliaries. For an oracle says that when a man of brass or iron guards the State, it will be destroyed. Such is the tale; is there any possibility of making our citizens believe it?"

"Not in the present generation; there is no way of accomplishing this; but their sons may be made to believe in the tale, and their sons' sons, and posterity after them."

"I see the difficulty; yet the fostering of such a belief will make them care more for the city and for one another. Enough, however, of the fiction, which may now fly abroad upon the wings of rumour, while we arm our earthborn heroes, and lead them forth under the command of their rulers. Let them look round and select a spot whence they can best suppress insurrection, if any prove refractory within, and also defend themselves against enemies, who like wolves may come down on the fold from without; there let them encamp, and when they have encamped, let them sacrifice to the proper gods and prepare their dwellings."

Republic, iii, 414.

Before relating this passage to our general thesis there is one point in it that needs elucidation. An unwary reader might suppose that Plato envisages a free movement of individuals between the various classes, and that thus, though he believes in the maintenance of a class-divided State, he supposes that by some fortunate automatism every individual will find his rightful place in it. In fact he was much too realistic to admit any such dangerous freedom into his ideal of the State. A little later on (par. 434) he expressly excludes the interpretation that any large migration from the lower classes to the upper is intended. "Any meddlesome interchange between the three classes would be most mischievous to the State and could properly be described as the height of villainy."

To return to the general discussion of the passage. It belongs to the same historical context as the passages already quoted from Critias and Isocrates. But it is to be taken more seriously. Critias and Isocrates say what they suppose old lawgivers to have done; Plato announces what he would do himself if he could. And it is to be remembered that this is Plato now in his fifth decade, the Plato who has returned from his travels and begun the organization of what was to be his life's work, the Plato who has just opened the Academy. To Plato it comes naturally, and leaves no bad taste in his mouth, to use the name of God to lend authority to his fiction, to support his fiction by oracles, and to enjoin that the victims of the lie should be strict in the performance of their religious duties. If any citizen should mistake the import of the instruction that all the citizens are brothers and imagine it to conflict with the class division of society, he must be told that "God has framed you differently." If any ruler should be careless in maintaining the class-system, he is to be told that "God proclaims it as a first principle that it should be maintained, and that there is an oracle, etc." And when the citizens, at the word of command, have run off to select the spot whence they can best suppress insurrection, if any prove refractory within, they are to sacrifice to the *proper Gods*.

Even in antiquity there were people who could not breathe this air. Epicurus, who did not like Plato, called him, with obvious allusion to this famous fiction, "The Golden Man." And in our times, summing up his criticism of the *Republic*, J. M. Robertson writes (*A Short History of Free Thought*, 3rd ed., p. 175): "In that brilliant performance Plato objects to the scandalous tales in the poets concerning the Gods and the sons of Gods; but he does not object to them as being untrue. His position is that they are unedifying. For his own part he proposes that his ideal rulers frame new myths which shall edify the young: in his Utopia it is part of the business of the legislator to choose the right fictions; and the systematic imposition of an edifying body of pious fable on the general intelligence is part of his scheme for the regeneration of society. Honesty is to be built up by fraud, and reason by delusion. What the Hebrew Bible-makers did, Plato proposed to do."

In the *Laws*, the work of Plato's extreme old age (completed in point of subject-matter though lacking revision in point of style when he died in his eighty-first year), the effect produced by this policy of public deception is the more painful inasmuch as the verve and brilliance of the earlier work, which help to carry off the more paradoxical opinions, are lacking, and their place has been taken by a weariness of spirit and torment of the soul. It contains, indeed, early in the fifth book, a solemn tribute to the importance of truth. "Truth is the beginning of every good thing, both to Gods and men; and he who would be blessed and happy, should be from the first a partaker of the truth, that he may live a true man as long as possible, for then he can be trusted; but that man is not to be trusted who loves voluntary falsehood, and he who loves involuntary falsehood is a fool. Neither condition is enviable; for the untrustworthy or the ignorant man has no friend, and as time goes on his character becomes known, and he lays up in store for himself isolation in crabbed age when life is on the wane; with the result that, whether his children and friends are alive or dead, he is equally solitary." But that Plato did not regard the "pious fiction" as a derogation from the truth the rest of the work makes clear.

Thus, in the second book, after a severe criticism of the popular taste in art, Plato observes that, in the matter of ethics, there is nothing to surprise us in the fact that only the highest and most philosophical minds can grasp the fundamental truth that Virtue is Happiness. Yet this truth must be the basis of our education; for only a State in which the inhabitants are utterly and irrevocably impressed with the truth of this judgment can hope to be law-abiding and happy. "And even if it were not true," he goes on to say, "still no lawgiver, if he ventured on a lie, could invent a more useful lie than this, nor one which would have better effect in making the citizens do what is right, not under compulsion but voluntarily."

What is distressing in this passage is not simply the approval of the lie. It is, rather, the identification of virtue with obedience to the law. The purpose of Plato was the complete absorption of the individual in the citizen. He demands a perfect loyalty from every citizen to the constitution; but since the lots of the citizens under the constitution are not going to be equally fortunate (and everywhere both in the *Republic* and in the *Laws* he is haunted by the question of internal revolution) he can only secure this unquestioning obedience by the imposition of

99

the belief that the constitution is the law of God, and that obedience to it is synonymous with virtue. From the Platonic point of view the *Antigone* contained the most dangerous doctrine, and it was precisely such teaching (and not, as some have imagined, a debased type of drama that has disappeared) which necessitated Plato's opposition to the poets.

Having raised again the question of the useful lie, Plato proceeds with one of his most cynical observations. The general belief in myths, he points out, is a proof that you can make people believe anything if you have a mind to. Accordingly what the legislator has to do is to reflect what belief will be of the greatest public advantage, and then use all his efforts to make the community utter one and the same theme in all their songs and tales and discourses all their life long, with a view to impressing it indelibly on their minds. Of course Plato meant to benefit the community as a whole and individually. But does this intention make his policy any the wiser? Incidentally it may be observed that one consequence of such a policy, the complete suppression of all originality in art, was envisaged by Plato and received his hearty approval. The Egyptians, he triumphantly points out, have stereotyped their art. Why cannot we?

Plato, while approving the use of the pious fiction, was above all things anxious to avoid "the lie in the soul." But whether the habitual employment of the one does not carry with it the nemesis of the other is a question that may well be raised when we come to ask what, of all the religious institutions Plato proposed to establish in the *Laws*, he really and sincerely believed himself. Others must answer this question for themselves; for myself I avow that I can put no kinder interpretation on the religious legislation of the *Laws* than this, that Plato sincerely meant to prescribe what would benefit his fellow-men in this world and the next, but that by the end of his life the employment of the pious fiction had become so much a second-nature with him that he himself could not say what, if any, of it he believed, or what belief meant as distinct from a feeling that the *credo* would be socially useful.

The religious beliefs and practices recommended in the *Laws* fall into two main categories: first, a reactionary reimposition of a mass of traditional cults; second, the imposition of a startlingly new and intellectually defended body of theological dogmas. Failure to conform to either category of belief is to be punished with imprisonment for a first offence, then death.

Although in his second book Plato had sarcastically referred to the general belief in myths as proof that you could get the people to believe anything, he does not scruple in the fourth book to recommend the maintenance of all the traditional beliefs on no better foundation than that of "ancient report" (παλαιὸς λόγος, iv, 715e). God, he says, not man, as Protagoras maintained, is the measure of all things. For the good man to offer sacrifice to the gods, and hold converse with them by means of prayers and offerings and every kind of service, is the noblest of all things, and also the most conducive to a happy life. First in honour are to be held the Olympian gods, then the gods of the underworld; then demi-gods, heroes, and private and ancestral gods; and lastly comes the honour of parents living or dead.

In the tenth book he returns to the subject with violence, upbraiding the young atheists of the day, who did not find in "ancient report" sufficient foundation for belief:

"Who can be calm when he is called upon to prove the existence of the gods? Who can avoid hating and abhorring

the men who are and have been the cause of this argument?
I speak of those who will not believe the words which
they have heard as babes and sucklings from their mothers
and nurses, repeated by them both in jest and earnest like
charms; who have heard also and seen their parents offering
up sacrifices and prayers—sights and sounds delightful to
children—sacrificing, I say, in the most earnest manner on
behalf of them and of themselves, and with eager interest
talking to the gods and beseeching them as though they
were firmly convinced of their existence; who likewise see
and hear the genuflexions and prostrations which are made
by Hellenes and barbarians to the rising and setting sun
and moon, in all the various turns of good and evil fortune,
not as if they thought that there were no gods, but as if
there could be no doubt of their existence, and no suspicion
of their non-existence; when men, knowing all these things,
despise them on no real grounds, as would be admitted
by all who have any particle of intelligence, and when they
force us to say what we are now saying, how can any one
in gentle terms remonstrate with the like of them, when
he has to begin by proving to them the very existence of
the gods?"

Laws, x, 887–888.

Plato himself was obviously not convinced by this torrent
of angry nonsense; for though it would be natural to
suppose that the question with which the passage above
concludes was a mere rhetorical question to which no
answer was required, Plato at once proceeds, "Yet the
attempt must be made." But the astounding thing is that
when the attempt is made it consists not at all of a justification of the traditional cults of Olympian deities, gods
of the underworld, demi-gods, heroes, and private and

ancestral gods. These cults are left without a further word of justification, but in addition to them there is now introduced, by an elaborate and dubious argument, a new type of god, the astral deities of the East.

Plato couples his demonstration of the divinity of the heavenly bodies with an examination of the materialist philosophy of Ionia, and a statement of his own position in face of it, which is among the most interesting and important passages in his writings. A full examination of it would only be in place here if our intention were to proceed to a similarly full examination of the physical theories of Epicurus and Lucretius. But its importance for the purpose of our study is that it reveals to us the fact that in leaving the established cults without rational justification, and turning to the rational justification of a new type of religion, worship of the astral deities, Plato's action is determined by the necessity to find an answer to the "atheism" of the Ionian philosophers. Here, as elsewhere, they are the object of attack. The specific type of atheism found among the physical philosophers was either the belief that there are no gods at all, or the belief that they take no interest in human affairs. This latter is the belief that later came to be accepted as the characteristic view of Epicureanism. It could more precisely be defined as the dissociation of the gods from any control of the universe we inhabit; the belief that earth, sun, moon, and stars, are purely natural bodies whose motions are all to be explained in terms of natural law. This scientific view Plato found wholly incompatible with the political religion he proposed to establish.

Plato's argument for the divinity of the astral bodies is a curiosity. There are, he tells us, ten different kinds of motion in the universe. The first nine, which need not be enumerated, are all of external origin, communicated motions, capable of passing on their motion to other bodies, but always in the last resort dependent on the initial impulse received from outside. The tenth kind of motion, which differs from all the rest, is that which is capable of moving both others and itself. It is an original, spontaneous source of motion, the true principle of motion and change in all that is.

If this power of self-moving be found in any material substance, simple or compound, whether it be earthy, watery, fiery, airy, or a mixture of two or more of these, we say that the thing is alive; and we call the self-moving power in it the life. This life, or self-moving power, is the soul. The soul may be defined as a motion that moves itself.

The principle of motion, the motion that moves itself, having been identified as soul, is now made to carry with it all the connotations of the Greek word Psyche. To enumerate some of them: the motion that moves itself, the source of all life in the universe, is identical with wishes, reasonings, opinions true and false, attention, deliberation, joy and sorrow, confidence, fear, hatred, love. It is such motions as these, then, that control the secondary, derivative motions of corporeal substances, such as earth, sun, moon, and stars.

That the soul that moves the world is a good soul, a principle of wisdom and virtue, is shown by the regularity of the motions it initiates. Above all, the absolute regularity of the motions of the sun, moon, planets, and the heaven of the fixed stars is proof of the goodness of the souls that move them. We may surrender then, says Plato, to the physical philosophers the body of the sun and moon, and accept in that sense the truth of their assertions that sun and moon are made of fire and earth. Yet though every man sees the body of the sun, no man sees its soul. But it is the soul of the sun, the principle of motion in it, that is the sun-god, and in this sense the ancients have been right to worship sun and moon, and we must still continue the old wise ways.

One feels in the movement of the sentences that Plato had some feeling of triumph as he came to the end of this demonstration. But he had despaired of human nature. He therefore did not deceive himself as to the likelihood of there still being persons who would both fail to be convinced of the desirability of worshipping the stars, or who, if they accepted these strange gods, might still fail to see how the successful demonstration of the new theology carried with it the necessity of rendering unquestioned conformity to the old worship of the Olympian gods, the gods of the under-world, the demi-gods, the heroes, and the rest. Plato, therefore, had to provide for them. He established a court of inquisition, the Nocturnal Council, to deal with heretics, which was to allot five years' imprisonment for a first offence, death for a second. Thus the advocacy of persecution for opinion made its first entry on the European scene. But there were already men in Plato's day capable of seeing that verbal logic about "motion that moves itself" was no substitute for a mechanical interpretation of the movements of the heavenly bodies; that the identification of a "motion that moves itself" with the life principle (*psyche*) was an empty phrase; that an analysis that identified the motion of the heavenly bodies with the motion of a living animal was so superficial as to be beneath contempt; that the ascribing to the "motion that moves itself" all the rich connotations of the Greek word *psyche* was a gross logical error springing from a total failure to understand the historical development of language and its symbolic function; and that the consequences of all this disastrous logic were fatal to the cause of human progress through knowledge of nature.

[1] A Croiset, *Les démocraties antiques*, p. 20.
[2] A. E. Taylor, *Platonism*, pp. 67, 68.

CHAPTER NINE

THE REVOLT FROM THE RELIGION OF THE CITY-STATE

Why Plato provided for two types of religion, (1) the traditional anthropomorphic gods, (2) new astral deities. Aristotle's explanation. The attitude to the City-State of Cynics, Stoics, and Epicureans.

As we have seen, in the *Laws* Plato provides for the establishment of two types of religion. First, he re-enacts all the traditional cults of the City-State; secondly, he introduces a new astral religion. In connection with the latter he attempts a formal theological proof of his creed and thus became the founder of natural theology. Why did he wish to establish two types of religion? Why did the latter only receive formal proof?

In a learned discussion of Plato's religious legislation Dr. Friedrich Solmsen writes:

"It seems certain that what Plato aims at in this book (*Laws*, x) is a restoration of the gods to their old position and dignity. He wishes them to become once again πολιοῦχοι or θεοὶ πολῖται as in the old city state. . . . The difficulty which is involved in this attempt and which makes it look slightly paradoxical, is that the gods whom he seeks to put in the traditional place are no longer Father Zeus or Pallas Athene, who, from their nature, might well indeed be πολιοῦχοι, but a wholly new kind of religious beings, namely, astral deities. In the course of a very elaborate demonstration, sun, moon, and the stars come to be described as embodiments of the divine soul and in themselves divine. But if this is so and if they are expected to take the place previously reserved for the Olympian gods, the question remains how these deified heavenly bodies can possibly fulfil the political functions of the old gods. . . ."

"It is clear, I think," he concludes, "that Plato has used some violence in assigning a political task to his new cosmic deities."[1]

Dr. Solmsen has, in part, created his own problem. The new astral deities were not intended, as he supposes, "to take the place previously reserved for the Olympian gods." As we have seen, Plato expressly re-enacts the worship of the Olympian gods, along with that of many other traditional deities. The question, then, is not Why did Plato try to substitute a new type of god for the old?, but Why did he wish to establish the worship of both?

The answer is that the two types of religion were to suit two types of worshippers, on the old Egyptian model. The traditional forms of worship were for the mass of the people; the educated worshippers were expected to give serious intellectual assent only to the new astral gods. For the people, the traditional myths; for the governors, the new theology, a rationally justified science of the divine ($\tau\grave{o}$ $\theta\epsilon\hat{\iota}ov$). Plato does not, of course, say this in so many words; it was one of the more embarrassing parts of his task; but this interpretation is necessitated by the whole logic of his thought. Nor indeed is it denied by Plato's apologists; it is merely left unsaid. Thus Taylor, giving Plato the credit for the invention of Natural Theology, says: "Natural theology, then, meant originally a doctrine about God which is neither imaginative fiction nor socially useful fiction but science, and such a doctrine was attempted for the first time by Plato in the *Laws*."[2] But he omits to remind us, indeed in the passages I have previously quoted he seems expressly to deny, that Plato also inculcated socially useful fictions. So again when, in discussing Plato's equivocal use of the words *gods* and *god*, Taylor tells us that "Plato was *personally* a monotheist," those who dwell on the significance of the word "personally" will have no difficulty in completing the thought—"but politically an idolater."

That the new astral deities were only intended for the governing class is proved by the educational programme of the *Laws*. According to it education has two branches, gymnastic for the body, "music" for the soul. In gymnastic the practical end of fitness for war must be the regulating principle. "Music" comprises reading, writing, playing the lyre, arithmetic, geometry, and some astronomy. The treatment of education in the *Laws* is so valuable as a whole that one would like to add one's voice to those who now advocate that it would be well if our Faculties of Education would substitute it, in their curricula, for the altogether less comprehensive and less mature discussion in the *Republic*. But valuable as it is, it has its own striking limitations. It is not so much a scheme of studies as, to use a current phrase, of Safe Studies. For reading for educational purposes, in spite of the abundant literature of Greece, Plato can hardly find anything to recommend. It is unnecessary here to do more than refer to his quarrel with the poets. But the question of prose-writers was equally difficult, for they all exhibited in greater or less degree the corrupting influence of Ionia. Plato can only recommend as a suitable type of literature that on which he is at present engaged, the *Laws*. He modestly suggests that it is divinely inspired, and recommends that teachers who cannot conform to this type of instruction should be dismissed (Bk. vii, 810–812). As regards non-literary subjects, the higher branches of mathematics are not for the general body even of the citizens, but for the few. Astronomy, in particular, raises special difficulties. It is undesirable, indeed it is impious, to seek into the nature of the Most High God and the whole universe, and to meddle with the quest for causes. But there is a certain sense in which astronomy is an aid to religion, and to this extent it should be taught (vii, 821).

The point at issue here is historically of interest, and it is also of importance for the understanding of our special subject. Plato, as we have seen, thought that the motion of the heavenly bodies was the effect of soul. Owing to the Pythagorean superstitions concerning mathematics in which he was deeply involved, it seemed to him that the goodness of the Soul that moved the heavenly orbs was proved by their moving in perfect circles at regular speeds. In crying disaccord with this view of the universe was the observed behaviour of the planets, the Vagabond Stars. Plato had therefore set it as a problem in the Academy to account for the irregularities of the observed movements of the planets on the assumption that, in spite of appearances, they were in fact moving in circles at uniform speed. A mathematical solution of this problem had recently been produced by Eudoxus. This seemed to Plato such a crushing defeat for the Ionian astronomers that he was prepared to risk teaching astronomy to selected students up to a point that would enable them to understand the demonstration of Eudoxus (Bk. viii, 821–822).

Our view that the two types of religion recommended by Plato had reference to the class-division of the State is thus borne out by his educational programme, in which it is clear that only the most promising students, marked out for high administrative positions, are to have sufficient education to understand the full force of his attack on Ionian science and the full justification for his new astral theology. The rest will worship in the old traditional way. That this was also the view Aristotle took of Plato's meaning is made clear by an unusually candid passage in his own great work on theology (*Metaphysics*, xi (xii), 8, 13, p. 1074*b*). There he speaks about the ancient tradition that the heavenly bodies are divine, and says that this should be received. But as for gods in human shape and in the shape of other animals, and all similar traditions, these are "myths that have been introduced to persuade the multitude, and on account of their utility in regard of social custom and the public good." Aristotle had been Plato's pupil in the Academy for twenty years. It is conclusive, then, for our argument that he takes precisely the same view of the function of the popular mythology recommended in the *Laws* as Isocrates had taken of the animal gods of Egypt.

The candour of Aristotle's admission has been matter of surprise. But unless Aristotle had a political enemy listening to his course of lectures he ran little risk. A disavowal of belief in the popular myths would hardly be an offence in the aristocratic circles of the Lyceum behind closed doors. Indeed, an understanding of the function assigned by Aristotle to these myths would be an essential part of the education of a gentleman. The offence would arise only if such secrets of government were uttered in the market-place.

It is precisely this sense of the alienation of the philosophy of the Platonic and Aristotelian schools from the interests of the humbler folk that is the characteristic of the three schools that next arose in Athens: the Cynics, the Stoics, and the Epicureans.

Of the first it has been said that they "formulated a doctrine which especially appealed to those who felt themselves simple and oppressed, and which has been well described as 'the philosophy of the proletariat of the Greek world.' "[3] And this certainly seems a fair enough comment upon the views of the Cynic Diogenes of Sinope, who took to the staff and the wallet, the symbols of the wandering beggar's life; who threw away his cup, when he saw a child drinking with his hand from the brook, with the remark, "That boy has taught me a lesson"; who, when he saw at Megara sheep protected by leather jackets while children went bare, said, "It is better to be a Megarian's ram than his son"; and who, when asked to what city he belonged, contemptuously rejected all connexion with the civilization of the city-state, by saying that he was a citizen of the world. Nor was it only aliens in Greece, like the immigrant from Sinope, who belonged to this school. It was from a distinguished family in Thebes that Crates came who, in order that he might break with the tradition of his class and take to the wallet and staff, first sold his property for two hundred talents and distributed the money among his friends.

But it was not only of the Cynics that it was true to write, as Arnold does,[4] "they were intensely antipathetic to men of the type of Plato and Aristotle, whose whole life was bound up with pride in their country, their birth, and their literary studies." It was also true, if not to the same extent, of the Stoics. Thus it was as a counterblast to Plato's *Republic* that Zeno, the founder of Stoicism, wrote his *Republic*, in which he said that the ideal State must embrace the whole world; that its laws must be those which are prescribed by Nature, not by convention; that it should have no images nor temples, as these are unworthy of the deity, and no sacrifices, as he cannot be pleased by costly gifts; no gymnasia, for its youth must not waste their time in idle exercises; and no division of the people into classes, for all alike will be wise men. Such was Zeno's very un-Platonic notion of what the ideal State would be. Significant also is the fact that his disciple Persaeus wrote a reply to Plato's *Laws*; while the man who was called the Second Founder of the School, Cleanthes of Assos, was not only a proletarian but proud of it. Criticized by men of independent means for his presumption in thinking that a labourer could be a philosopher, he defended himself by thrusting out a handful of small coin with the remark, "Cleanthes could support a second Cleanthes, if he wished; but gentlemen live on others, and are yet but sorry philosophers."

But neither Cynicism nor Stoicism had sufficiently analysed the aristocratic philosophies to be able to offer effective resistance. Cynicism was very largely a negative revolt from civilization innocent of any comprehensive philosophy. The Stoics did attempt to offer an alternative to the ideology of the oligarchical faction in the city-states of Greece, but it had no foundation in science and could not last. The ultimate destiny of Stoicism, like that of Christianity later, was to become the mainstay of the type of society it had begun by attacking. The Stoics were even more deeply involved in astral superstition than Plato. It is true that, unlike Plato, they never conceived so desperate a hope as that the starry gods of the sky could be made in any sense or degree to take upon them the function of the old city gods of the particularistic Greek States. On the contrary, they saw in the new astral religion the means of superseding the local cults which fostered hostility between city and city in Greece, and it was the universality of their religion that made it suitable for adoption by the world empire of Rome. But, as we shall see later, Stoicism proved compatible with a high degree of superstition, and the acquiescence of its later exponents in the policy of deceiving the multitude fitted it to perform for an empire the social function performed by the local gods in the older city-state.

The Stoic teachers, nearly all of them non-Greeks, coming from Asiatic towns in which Greek and non-Greek had mingled for generations and created a common civilization, had no patience with the truculent parochialism of Plato and Aristotle. "Plato said that all barbarians were enemies by nature; it was proper to wage war upon them, even to the point of enslaving or extirpating them. Aristotle said that all barbarians were slaves by nature, especially those of Asia; they had not the qualities which entitled them to be free men, and it was proper to treat them as slaves."[5] The Stoics endeavoured to rid Athenian philosophy of these shamefully narrow conceptions, sponsored by the Academy and the Lyceum, by their appeal to Nature. Life according to Nature was to supersede life according to the particular traditions of each locality.

But what was this knowledge of Nature, the laws of which the Stoics were so confident they possessed? It was an amalgam of Greek and Oriental speculation, grandiose in its general conception but excluding the very possibility of science. Out of the Greek tradition of philosophy, which they did not understand, they selected the obscure wisdom of Heracleitus and amalgamated it with the astral fatalism of the Chaldeans. "The fundamental dogma of astrology, as the Greeks conceived it, is that of the solidarity of the universe. The world forms a vast organism of which all the parts are united by an incessant interchange of molecules or effluences. The stars, inexhaustible generators of energy, act continuously on the earth and on man—on man who is an epitome of the whole of Nature, the microcosm of which each element is in correspondence with some part of the starry sky. Such in two words is the theory formulated by the Stoic disciples of the Chaldeans."[6]

This Stoic brand of astral theology completed and superseded that advocated by Plato in the *Laws*. It had many advantages. In the first place it was applied to a nobler purpose, the promotion of the brotherhood of mankind, instead of the well-being of a class-divided city-state of 5,040 citizens, the magic number approved by Plato. In the second place it had behind it all the prestige of an imagined antiquity: the Chaldean priests were supposed to have devoted tens of thousands of years to the elaboration of its doctrines. And in the third place it was actually more imposing intellectually than Plato's essay. Cumont (*op. cit.*) makes for it the claim that Taylor makes for Plato's system: "Astrology was in truth the first scientific theology. The logic of Hellenism co-ordinated the Oriental doctrines, combined them with the Stoic philosophy and made of them a system of incontestable grandeur, an ideal reconstruction of the universe, the boldness and power of which inspire in Manilius, when he is not exhausted by the difficulties of his intractable material, accents both convinced and sublime:

"Quis caelum possit, nisi caeli munere, nosse
    et reperire deum, nisi qui pars ipse deorum, est."

("Who could understand the heaven, except by the favour of heaven, or find God, if he had not himself some part in the divine.")

On the basis of this sort of science of Nature it was hoped to renew the civilization of the Graeco-Roman world. Cicero reveals to us this ideal in a passage of the *de Finibus* (chap. xxii, 73): "The Stoics pay as much honour to physics (i.e. their science of Nature) as they do to logic, for the very good reason that the man who is to live in accordance with Nature must start from a knowledge of the whole universe and its administration. For indeed nobody can pass a true judgment on good and evil unless he understands the whole science of Nature and the manner of life of the gods, and unless he knows whether or not the nature of man accords with that of the universe. Furthermore, the ancient precepts of the wise men, who admonish us *To bow to Time, To follow God, To know oneself, To do nothing to excess*—no one can appreciate the importance of these precepts, and they are supremely important, without a knowledge of physics. And this is the one science also that can inform us what the efficacy of nature is in helping us to practice justice and to be loyal in friendship and the other ties that bind men to their fellows. Indeed, even devotion to the gods, and the extent of the debt of gratitude we owe to them, are unintelligible without instruction in the laws of nature." Such were the exaggerated hopes that were based on a "science" which experience has proved to be more fruitful of superstition than of knowledge.

Stoicism contributed to man's understanding of his world the conception of the solidarity of the universe. It contributed to his political advancement a concept that seemed to the Stoics to depend on this, that of the solidarity of the human race. But it could not long be an instrument of progress. Its encouragement of divination opened the door to a superstition that debauched the intelligence of mankind. Its absence of any real scientific insight precluded the possibility of progress in positive knowledge. The inner heart of its teaching, that harmony already reigns in the universe if one could only perceive it, turns man away from the struggle with Nature. Not the effort to alter external circumstances, but the effort to adapt oneself to them, is all that it calls forth. Its highest fruit was resignation, whether exhibited by the emperor or the slave.

[1] "The Background of Plato's Theology," *Transactions of the American Philological Association*, vol. lxvii, 1936.

[2] *Op. cit.*, p. 99.

[3] Gomperz, *Greek Thinkers*, ii, p. 148.

[4] *Roman Stoicism*, p. 50.

[5] Tarn, *Alexander the Great and the Unity of Mankind*, p. 4.

[6] Cumont, *Religions Orientales dans le Paganisme Romain*.

CHAPTER TEN

WHAT EPICURUS DID

Professor Cornford and the twilight of Greek philosophy. Plato and the Oracle of Apollo. Epicurus founds the first organized movement to combat superstition.

It is customary with historians of philosophy to class Stoics and Epicureans together as characteristic of the decline of Greek philosophy. Thus Professor Cornford, in his widely read book, *Before and After Socrates*, writes: "These later philosophies are beyond my province. I mention them because I cannot resist the temptation to round off the analogy I drew at an earlier stage. In pre-Socratic science we saw something of the attitude of wondering childhood; and in certain utterances of the Sophists we heard the accent of adolescent rebellion against authority. In Socrates, Plato, and Aristotle Greek philosophy grows to the maturity of responsible manhood and the fullness of intellectual power. But the extravagance of the intellect seems destined to overreach itself as surely as the extravagance of the myth-making imagination. Then nothing remains but the philosophy of old age, the resignation of a twilight that deepens alike over the garden of Pleasure and hermitage of Virtue."

This reduction of the great intellectual effort of Greece to the same futility as the extravagances of the myth-making imagination seems unworthy of Professor Cornford's own many splendid services to the cause of reason. Unhappily neither this nor the estimate of the relative importance and of the significance of the various Greek schools is peculiar to him. It represents an all but universal judgment on the history of Greek thought, and one which robs it of its inspiration for our age. Must we accept it as true?

For myself, I think not. The pre-Socratic philosophers were not children, nor was their world young, nor their civilization unsophisticated. They were the heirs of a culture already then at least as old as Christianity is now, who renewed it by a revolutionary approach to Nature and were conscious of their originality.

In the Sophists it is difficult to catch the accents of adolescent rebellion against authority. In Protagoras we rather hear the accents of a man who was profoundly influenced by the Ionian revolution of thought, and who realized that its acceptance implied a revolutionary change in Greek political life. The kernel of his thought is his realization of the interpenetration of science and politics, and he chose to make himself a vehicle of enlightenment. That in so doing he, like Anaxagoras, got himself into political hot water prepares us for the next stage in the history of Greek thought.

Plato does not represent Greek thought in the maturity of responsible manhood and the fullness of intellectual power. He was assuredly a man of very great mental ability and rich spiritual gifts; but he is not on the same high level as the great men of the fifth century, Aeschylus, Hippocrates, Thucydides. In Greek philosophy he represents a political reaction against Ionian enlightenment, in the interest of an ideal of a slave-owning, class-divided, chauvinistic city-state which was already an anachronism. While his Ionian predecessors had disinfected all that they borrowed from the civilizations of the Near East of its taint of superstition and sacerdotalism, Plato took from Chaldea a belief in the divinity of the stars and from Egypt a technique of mental repression. He conducted a life-long war against all that was most vital in Greek culture—the poetry of Homer, the natural philosophy of Ionia, and the drama of Athens.

It was Plato's habit to voice these hostilities through the "novelized" character of Socrates. How far Plato invented the character of Socrates is an insoluble problem. But he was no Boswell concerned to paint a meticulously accurate historical portrait; whatever historical elements his portrait may contain, it is of the painter it gives us reliable evidence, not of the subject. The Socrates of the *Dialogues* is the contribution of Plato to thought, not of Socrates. And there is that in the portrait which strikes at the roots of philosophy, as the Ionians conceived it. It was the habit of the Delphic priesthood, a centre of oligarchic reaction in the Greek world, to issue from time to time a pronouncement on the ideal type of man and citizen. It was thus that the peasant Myson, and Clearchus of Methydrion, were exalted into models for the imitation of Greece—"living symbols," as Nilsson puts it, "of the subordination Apollo required." Socrates, Plato's Socrates, was such another. He is recommended to us from the outset as the man whom the oracle of Apollo had selected as the wisest man in Greece. This guaranteeing of the wisdom of Socrates as sound because it had received the divine approval of Apollo through the lips of his laurel-chewing priestess is an insult to the thought of the preceding two hundred years. It is the negation of what was the specific originality of Greek thought, namely, that it was an effort of the human intelligence to interpret Nature directly unaided by revelation. In the last resort Plato casts us back on oracles or "ancient report."

As for Aristotle, his great contribution to mankind was made after he left the Academy, and, specifically, after he had rejected the tendency of the Academy to substitute

mathematics for natural philosophy. But he retained from
Platonism the conviction that science is the concern only
of a leisured élite, and is possible for them only if leisure
is secured by slavery. He therefore never contemplated the
dissemination of science among the masses; and his scientific effort is conditioned by the fact that it is divorced
from the productive side of life. Its mainspring is curiosity,
not service. To know was Aristotle's ambition, not to do.
These limitations are relevant to the question whether
Aristotle represents Greek thought at its most mature and
responsible level.

Finally, when Professor Cornford talks of the Stoic school
as the "hermitage of Virtue" and the Epicurean school as
the "garden of Pleasure," he promotes the illusion that the
tiny city-states, for which Plato and Aristotle stood, were
the *sine qua non* of public-spirited activity on the part of
the individual; as if the selfish little oligarchic city-state of
the type Plato admired in Sparta, or of the type Aristotle
had seen in Asia, in which "a small aristocracy of Greek
citizens ruled over a barbarian peasantry who cultivated
the land for their masters and had no share in the State"[1]
—as if this were a nobler ideal than that of the well-being
of the inhabited world as a whole, which had replaced it
in the politics of Macedon and the philosophies of the Porch
and the Garden.

But if Zeno and Epicurus are justly to be compared with
one another in their freedom from the narrow horizons
of the city-state, the putting of their philosophies otherwise
on an equal footing (and indeed it is more usual to incline
the balance in favour of Zeno) is hardly justified, and seems
a misreading of the history of Greek thought—natural
enough, of course, in those who think Plato was the crown
of it.

This is obvious, from the outset, in the relation in which they stood to their predecessors in Greek philosophy. Zeno raised the banner of Heracleitus, Epicurus that of—I will not say Democritus, for he found much to criticize in him, but of—atomism. This divergence of choice in itself puts an immeasurable gulf between the two systems; yet I find it generally regarded, in histories of philosophy, as of no significance. Each of the new thinkers is charged with having grabbed somewhat carelessly from the heritage of the past whichever physical theory he thought would best serve as a foundation for his ethical system. Now both systems had, as part of their common revolt from Platonism, the ideal of serving humanity as a whole and of constructing for the service of humanity a philosophy based on Nature. It becomes, therefore, of the utmost significance to consider the validity of the natural knowledge on which they respectively based their systems.

It is an assured conclusion of modern scholarship that Ionian philosophy represents not a random movement but an orderly development. It set before itself a problem, namely, the giving of a rational account of the constitution of the universe. It arrived at the triumphant solution of this problem with the elaboration of the atomic system of Leucippus and Democritus. The system of Heracleitus, however important, was but one of many stepping-stones on the way to this safe landing place. It follows that any later school that professes to base itself on the physical theories of Heracleitus, *ipso facto* also declares itself ignorant or incompetent in the domain of Greek natural philosophy; and this without doubt the Stoics were.[2] Epicurus's choice of atomism as the physical basis of his system is equally proof of his competence in this matter. His choice was not a random one but the best that could be made by one conversant with the whole previous history of Greek thought.

The specific task of Epicurus was to resume the full tradition of Ionian natural philosophy both as pure science and as a solvent of superstition, with the consciousness derived from the career of Anaxagoras and the Sophists that this task carried implications that were social and political as well as scientific, and with the knowledge that the views of the reaction had been set out at length by the Golden Man in his *Laws*.

Epicurus was born about 340 B.C., some seven or eight years after the death of Plato. He was the child of Athenian parents, but was probably born in the island of Samos, whither his parents had emigrated. At the age of eighteen he was in Athens. Then during a period of some ten years he is heard of at various towns in Asia Minor, notably Colophon and Teos; and it is supposed that it was at the latter town he met Nausiphanes who was then expounding the atomic system there. A year or two later, when he was thirty, he had settled in Mitylene. Here he gathered certain disciples about him and was recognized as a teacher of philosophy. His disciples included his own three brothers, which may be taken as proof that he was not so hard to get on with as might be implied by the abusive epithets he is said to have flung at other philosophers. Subsequently he transferred his school to Lampsacus (the town to which Anaxagoras had fled from Athens); and there it is obvious that his reputation and his system must already have been established, for we now hear the names of some of his most famous disciples: Metrodorus, Colotes, Polyaenus, Idomeneus, and Leonteus with his wife Themista.

Epicurus reversed the order of Anaxagoras' flight. When he was thirty-four years of age, in 307 B.C., he left Lampsacus for Athens, then under the government of Demetrius Poliorcetes. There he purchased a house and the famous Garden, and there he remained for thirty-seven years, till his death, as head of the school he had established. At Athens he made new disciples, among whom were Hermarchus of Mitylene, Pythocles, and a brother of Metrodorus, Timocrates by name, who afterwards left the brotherhood and circulated scandalous tales about it. A notable feature about the school was the inclusion of women and slaves among the members. Among the women were some of the courtesan class, the most notable being Leontion, who afterwards became the wife of Metrodorus. The life of the community was one of great simplicity and sobriety, but that, of course, did not prevent the multiplication of slanders.

"Vain is the word of a philosopher which does not heal any suffering of man." This is a characteristic saying of Epicurus, in which he resumes the Ionian tradition that love of mankind and love of science are twin-born. It was the master-conception of Epicurus that a true knowledge of the Nature of Things was the sovereign remedy for the ills of mankind, both individually and socially. To those who do not understand the conception it seems proof that he was basically uninterested in science and incapable of it. They say that he was primarily interested in ethics and only concerned with science in so far as it seemed to promote his ethical programme. What they fail to observe is that, in the view of Epicurus, unless the science be true it can serve no ethical, nor any other, purpose. It was Plato, not Epicurus, who thought that the remedy for human ills was the edifying lie.

In the Garden, therefore, the atomic system was the basis of the teaching. The atomic system provided a rational and

naturalistic account of the phenomena of the heavens. In
the Athens of Epicurus, in which the thunder and thunderbolt were alleged to be manifestations of the wrath of Zeus,
a naturalistic account of these phenomena could afford
great mental relief. Such a condition of mental relief the
Epicureans called *ataraxia*, and it was their object to promote
it. Another great source of mental unrest in the Athens
of the day was the dread of torments in the world to come.
On the depicting of these imaginary horrors Plato in the
Republic had expended all the resources of his graphic pen.
The atomic system taught that the soul does not survive
separation from the body, and that these terrors are therefore illusory. In this sense also it tended to promote *ataraxia*.

The purpose of the school was to convey this healing
balm to all that needed it. Epicurus did not believe in street-
preaching; but he taught that one must not refuse to lecture
when asked. Furthermore, he had not two types of doctrine,
one for the rulers and one for the ruled. There was one
science of Nature, and all had need of it. Accordingly in
his own school at Athens, and in the other Epicurean communities with which he was in touch, the study of atomism
as a cure for superstition began. The groups in the various
centres were organized on a regular basis with reference
to the progress of the members in the study of the system,
and they promised: "We will be obedient to Epicurus,
according to whom we have made it our choice to live."[3]
Epicurus wrote voluminously both to promote the higher
branches of the study and to produce handy manuals for
those without time or capacity to master all the details.
He is said to have written altogether some three hundred
scrolls. Such was the Life of the Master of the "Garden
of Pleasure."

It is the specific originality of Epicurus that he is the

first man known to history to have organized a movement for the liberation of mankind at large from superstition. The thing had been attempted before by the Ionian doctors, who seem to have taken it in their stride as a natural part of their work, and who seem not to have foreseen the strength of the opposition that their movement would encounter. But history had revealed how superficial was this view. It had become clear that not only popular superstition, or the selfish interests of a parcel of fraudulent oracle-mongers or magic-working quacks, opposed Ionian science. The fundamental opposition came from the structure of ancient society itself. The interests of the nobility, and their ideology, were radically hostile to the new view. The ignorance and the selfishness of the people (for the people too had their privileges to preserve as against the resident aliens and the slaves) also buttressed the traditional modes of thought. Furthermore, as the class-struggle in the Greek States persisted wearily from generation to generation, the possibility of employing superstition, erected into a state religion, as a principle of order and stability was more and more consciously realized and explored. With this came further corruption of mind and character. The noblest spirits were flawed and rang false. An analysis of the work of a soaring genius like Pindar discloses a complex of base and detestable superstitions. Language itself had been infected. Not a true scientific ethic but a selfish political expediency directed the employment of the terms virtuous or base. Finally, in the established schools of philosophy itself, it had become the accepted view that government of men was impossible except on the basis of a lie, and the most powerful intellect and impressive personality of the preceding generation had devoted his life to the elaboration of the wholesome and necessary lie that was to save

Greek society. In the interests of this lie he was preaching
the destruction of the books that contained the tradition
of Ionian wisdom. He was urging that his own fraudulent
book should be imposed by the State as the one and only
obligatory source of doctrine. He was advocating the
imprisonment and execution of those, not only who resisted
his nefarious plan, but who were honestly incapable of
giving mental assent to his freshly concocted doctrines.
Such were the circumstances under which Epicurus chose
his life's task. Such were the circumstances that determined
the specific form it was to take.

That such was the role of Epicurus was plainly enough
seen by the French critic Constant Martha in the sixties
of the last century; but owing to his inability to shake off
the prejudices that have traditionally obscured the significance of the Epicurean movement he was unable to
make his judgment stand out with the distinctness necessary to secure its general acceptance. His account, indeed,
is involved in a hopeless contradiction. He begins in the
traditional manner with a picture of Greece asleep under
the protectorate of the Macedonian kings, the collapse of
free institutions, and a citizen body given up to pleasure
and self-indulgence. In the general languor philosophy had
renounced lofty speculations and difficult researches. "Great
doctrines, like those of Plato and Aristotle, which moulded
at once citizens and sages, were far above the reach of this
degenerate indolence." In this enervating air arose various
new schools, of which the most seductive was that of
Epicurus. This quietist philosophy, in teaching men to lose
interest in politics, in religion, in science, in themselves,
had, as it were, disarmed them. "The ancient writers who
celebrate the innocence of the school, omit to remark that
it is the innocence of sleep."[4] Having preluded with this

stale variation on a hackneyed theme Martha, kindling his very alert intelligence by a personal survey of the then available evidence, contradicts all that he has said.

"What more learned systems had not dared to do entirely, Epicureanism did with a perfect finality and quiet decisiveness. Whatever its faults may have been, it expelled from nature, or rather gently escorted away, that infinity of celestial powers which merely embarrassed physics and morality" (p. 108).

"In expelling from nature the inept intervention of the gods of paganism, Epicurus also put an end to all those pious frauds by which men duped one another and duped themselves. While Pythagoras, Socrates, Democritus even, the Academy, the Lyceum, the Porch, all the schools, even the most free, believed in divination by the flight of birds, by the entrails of victims, by the stars, by dreams, by delirium and a hundred other means, Epicurus alone rejected these lying sciences and exposed the imposture. He constrained soothsayers and diviners to confess their own absurdity; he mocked the oracles to such good effect that in the end they dared not speak. It can be said that to-day a man passes for enlightened in proportion as he despises all that Epicurus despised" (p. 110).

"He was the first who made the effort to spread this enlightenment over the world" (p. 111).

"What we call educating the people is giving them such a training in natural philosophy as can lift them to the level of Epicureanism" (p. 111).

"Epicurus was the first to make the idea of natural law enter, I do not say into speculative philosophy, where it had reigned already for long, but into the imagination of the people" (p. 73).

Such is the amazing achievement which Martha (and with perfect justice) puts to the credit of the man whom he has just described as the most languid teacher of a languid age, a man whose genius it was to rob mankind of all his intellectual interests and lull him into the innocence of slumber. It is a pious service to the memory of a brilliant critic to disentangle what is original and well-founded in his criticism from what is traditional and false. Martha had at least the merit of seeing in Epicurus the first champion of popular enlightenment, the first organizer of a movement to free mankind at large from the fetters of superstition. He did not clearly see against what odds Epicurus had to contend; nor did he do justice to the vigorous effort of Epicurus to advance knowledge itself.

[1] Tarn, *op. cit.*, p. 4.

[2] Cf. Tarn, "Alexander, Cynics and Stoics" (*American Journal of Philology*, Jan. 1939), p. 54: "No Stoic before Poseidonius ever touched science."

[3] See *Organization and Procedure in Epicurean Groups*, N. de Witt, *Classical Philology*, July 1936.

[4] Constant Martha, *Le Poème de Lucrèce*, 2nd ed., 1873, pp. 1–12.

CHAPTER ELEVEN

EPICURUS AND PLATO

The Senses versus Reason. Physics versus Mathematics. The origin and nature of language. The attack on astral theology.

An echo of ancient controversy that has come down to us informs us that Epicurus was wont to refer to the head of the Academy as "the golden Plato." This obvious allusion to the notorious Royal Lie of the *Republic* in which Plato taught that the human race by divine ordinance was composed of three types, golden men like himself who were to legislate and govern, silver men to be the police and soldiers, and iron men to do the work, has been trivially misinterpreted as no more than an ironical comment on Plato's style![1] But the sarcasm sprang from deeper sources than literary jealousy. The opposition between Epicurus and Plato was as deep and fundamental as the opposition between Plato and the Ionian physicists. Epicurus was fighting for two causes to which Plato was relentlessly opposed, the Ionian scientific tradition and the spread of popular enlightenment. Plato was in a quite peculiar sense the object of his attack.

The justification for this attack is rarely appreciated in histories and handbooks of ancient philosophy, but it has occasionally been understood and expressed. A. W. Benn, for example, though he is the author of a brilliant analysis of the genuine contribution of Plato to human advancement, speaks on this point with a refreshing candour and humanity:

"The political constitution and code of Laws recommended by Plato to his new city are adapted to a great extent from the older legislation of Athens. As such they have supplied the historians of ancient jurisprudence with some valuable indications. But from a philosophic point of view the general impression produced is wearisome and even offensive. A universal system of espionage is established, and the odious trade of informer receives ample encouragement. Worst of all, it is proposed in the true spirit of Athenian intolerance, to uphold religious orthodoxy by persecuting laws. Plato had actually come to think that disagreement with the vulgar theology was a folly and a crime. One passage may be quoted as a warning to those who would set early associations to do the work of reason; and who would overbear new truths by a method which at one time might have been used with fatal effect against their own opinions."

Benn then quotes the passage from the *Laws* which we have printed on pages 101–102, and proceeds:

"Let it be remembered that the gods of whom Plato is speaking are the sun, moon, and stars; that the atheists whom he denounces only taught what we have long known to be true, which is that those luminaries are no more divine, no more animated, no more capable of accepting our sacrifices or responding to our cries than is the earth on which we tread; and that he attempts to prove the contrary by arguments which, even if they were not inconsistent with all that we know about mechanics, would still be utterly inadequate to the purpose for which they are employed.

"Supposing the atheist to be an entirely moral man, he is, on conviction, to be imprisoned for five years or more,

during which period he is to be constantly lectured by a
magistrate on the sinfulness of his unbelief; if at the end
of that period he comes to a proper frame of mind he is
to be released, but in case of relapse is to be put to death.
The vicious atheist or other heretic receives what, according
to our ideas, is a lighter punishment, imprisonment in
chains for life. It seems to be expected that he will not
long survive such treatment. Should a citizen be suspected
of practising private forms of devotion in his own house
or elsewhere, he is to be executed without a chance of
repenting. Those who believe that the gods can be propi-
tiated by prayer and sacrifice are to be punished, like the
wicked infidels, by perpetual imprisonment in chains.

"To quote Grote's admirable summary: 'The lawgiver
is the supreme and exclusive authority, spiritual as well as
secular. No dissenters from the orthodoxy prescribed by
him are admitted. Those who believe more than he does,
and those who believe less, however blameless their conduct, are condemned alike to pass through a long solitary
imprisonment to execution. Not only the speculations of
enquiring individual reason, but also the spontaneous in-
spirations of religious disquietude or terror, are suppressed
and punished.' I know not whether the atrocity of this
religious legislation is palliated or aggravated by the fact
that the legislator himself had probably no theological
belief."[2]

The religious legislation of the *Laws* has raised little
indignation among classical scholars, and its intimate connexion with the whole body of what is called the Platonic
system has been little explored; but if the English liberal
statesman of the nineteenth century, and the English
rationalist of the twentieth, were roused by it to indig-

nation and disgust, what warrant have we for supposing
that similar emotions were not roused among persons much
nearer to Plato in place and time than they? And how can
the history of ancient philosophy be written if this legislation be not given the crowning place in the philosophy
of Plato, to which it is certainly entitled as being the conclusion of his longest, latest, and ripest work?[3] In the
evolution of the theory of the *polis* at Athens the religious
legislation of Plato marks the natural culmination. It is the
mature expression of the mind of the Academy, which
aspired to be a training-ground for statesman in a city
where religious persecution had already been practised.

"If one described in a single phrase," writes Mr. Edwyn
Bevan, "why it is that the Hellenistic and the Roman world,
after political liberty is gone, seems to us for all the culture,
all the economic activity, all the virtue it still embodies,
to be steeped in a kind of dead atmosphere, an *aura morta*,
we may say that it is a world without causes. There were
no great modifications of terrestrial things which were to
be brought about by the corporate effort of some society
to which this or that man belonged." But Mr. Bevan has
missed the one great cause there was, the only one suited
to the age, the war upon superstition; and not simply on
superstition as a weakness of the human mind, but on superstition as recommended by philosophers and organized by
governments. And he has missed its champion, Epicurus.

To effect his purpose Epicurus needed to do more than
organize a society devoted to the extirpation of superstition.
He needed also to achieve a work of intellectual reconstruction. It was necessary not only to oppose the philosophic
tradition that ran down from Pythagoras, through Socrates,
to Plato, but also to refurbish the Ionian tradition where
it was unsuited to meet the fresh assault of Platonism. It

has been the habit to deny to Epicurus the credit of any such intellectual labour, in spite of his own statement that he found his happiness chiefly in such work.[4] But this is no longer possible. As the fragments of the writings of Epicurus are more carefully sifted and studied his importance in the realm of pure philosophy, as distinct from his influence as a moral and religious leader, is clearly recognized. He did not, as Martha supposed, simply withdraw from the field occupied by the Platonic and Aristotelian schools; he made to them a serious intellectual response.[5]

The first and essential point to challenge in the Platonic system (if we may call it a system; Plato did not) was its epistemology. Plato at first was of the opinion of Parmenides that reason alone was the guide to knowledge and that all sense-evidence must be rejected. He found the type of this *a priori* knowledge in geometry, and endeavoured to construct on this model a theory of ethics and politics, that is to say, a rule of life for the individual and for society. Thus it was that over the entrance of the Academy, the purpose of which was to train a philosophical governing class for Greece, he put up the warning: *You cannot enter here if you do not know geometry.*

At the back of his system lay the mystical idea that the soul is something alien to the material world in which it is temporarily imprisoned; that the fundamental truths of geometry, ethics, and politics are known to it in a previous existence; and that they can be "remembered" if we but practice the right technique. The imperfect circle we draw on the sand can never be the origin of the knowledge of the true relation of the length of the diameter to the circumference, but can at best only help us to discover these relations in ourselves, to "remember" them; and the science which assists this effort of memory is

134

geometry. So also the knowledge of truth, beauty, and goodness is not derived from experience, but is to be remembered by the aid of a new science, dialectics. Dialectics means discussion carried on in a rational way. The persistent endeavour to determine the true conditions of rational discussion brought to light important principles of logic, afterwards used by Aristotle as the foundation for the technique of logic which he devised. The preoccupation with geometry forwarded the progress of this science. These were notable contributions of the Academy to human knowledge.

But an enormous difficulty now presented itself. If all true science is of this *a priori*, non-experiential kind, what is the relation of this knowledge to the world in which, temporarily though it be, we actually do live? The growing sense of this difficulty is the origin of the changed point of view that manifests itself in the later dialogues of Plato. In the *Republic* and the *Phaedo* he does not scruple to teach that any influence of sense-impressions on the soul can only be for the bad. All true science must draw us away from the senses. Later, in the *Theaetetus*, he comes closer to reality and teaches that sense-data, though not in themselves knowledge, are the material of knowledge. Here he defines clearly the difference between sense-perception and thought, and his discussion constitutes an important contribution to the young science of psychology.

But Plato never achieved consistency on this point. *Iam de Platonis inconstantia longum est dicere* the Epicureans complained long ago.[6] While the necessity of coming to grips with Nature haunts the later Platonic dialogues, his educational programmes remained unaffected by it. Even in the *Laws* Nature is rigorously excluded from the curriculum. The subjects of education are to be Arithmetic, Geometry,

Astronomy, Harmonics, and Dialectic. And these terms did not mean quite what they mean to us. Arithmetic meant Theory of Numbers, not the practical arithmetic we learn at school. Geometry too was strictly divorced from practical applications; it was not a method of measuring things; it aimed at studying relations of space independent of number and measurement. Astronomy, inextricably entangled with astral theology, was not concerned with the physical constitution of the heavenly bodies; it was purely positional, and was in effect spherical geometry. Harmonics was the study of proportion. Dialectic, as we have seen, was an effort to arrive at truth by carrying on discussion according to certain rules that guaranteed consistency, but produced no new information. The idea that all these techniques are instruments for the investigation of Nature was wholly alien to the system. They were the gymnastic of the soul. And they were devised in good faith as the appropriate education for a governing class whose function it might be to supervise productive activities, but never to engage in them or to develop them.

The standpoint of Epicurus was utterly different. For him man, body and soul, was an organism which in the course of history had been produced on this earth. Man's senses were the instruments by which he acquired knowledge of his environment, that is the material world in which he lived. His mental faculties were one of the activities of the total organism, originating out of his sense-activities and having no meaning except in relation to the senses. All knowledge was knowledge of the material world, and progress in such knowledge could only be made by sticking close to the evidence of the senses. No technique of mathematics or logic was of any use except as a help to interpret or organize sense-evidence. The knowledge of how we ought to behave, whether as individuals or in society, was equally dependent on sense-perception. The basis of it all was sensations of pleasure or pain, or feelings of well-being or distress. Ethics and politics were branches of natural philosophy; they were man-made rules for behaviour, derived from experience, which ought to be altered whenever increased knowledge of Nature should teach man better ways of being at ease in mind and body. The essential of education was a knowledge of Nature, and a habit of strict attention to sense-evidence. Sense-evidence was always true so far as it goes, though endless errors arise in the interpretation of it.

This complete reversal of the Platonic programme is almost universally described in histories and handbooks as evidence of a total indifference to Greek culture. It is on the contrary the salvation of its most characteristic and vital element, its essential originality, the unique thing it contributed to the world, the pursuit of natural knowledge and the endeavour to base human life upon it. In support of their view the opponents of Epicureanism adduce a sentence which has survived from a letter addressed by Epicurus to Pythocles—"Up anchor, lad, and flee from every form of culture"—as if this meant anything but a thoroughly justifiable attack on the Culture with a capital C with which Greece was thoroughly infected. The true bearing of the notorious advice to Pythocles will be understood at once if the words be brought into relation with the defence of Natural Philosophy as against Culture which we have chosen to put upon the fly-leaf at the beginning of this book. The defence of a true culture in Epicurus is pervasive and profound. Let us take the classical epigram preserved in another Fragment: "We must not pretend to study philosophy, but really study it; for we do not need the appearance of health, but real health." Here speaks the man to whom culture and life were inseparable.

But those who charge Epicurus with hostility to culture have another argument which has been part of the stock-in-trade of his traducers since Plutarch. There was a distinguished mathematician in Greece called Polyaenus, whom we have already mentioned as one of those who had joined Epicurus when he was teaching in Lampsacus and before he had settled in Athens. This man was persuaded by Epicurus to give up geometry and become an Epicurean, that is to say an adherent of the physical theory of atomism. It is almost incredible that this should be triumphantly brought forward from that day to this as proof of the hostility of Epicurus to all advanced studies and difficult disciplines. It is proof of something very different. Is it to be supposed that a distinguished mathematician would abandon his subject at the bidding of an indolent anti-intellectual? If Epicurus persuaded Polyaenus to abandon mathematics for physics he did so, one must presume, because there was some opposition between the two. If mathematics in Greece had been at this time the handmaid of physical investigation, there could have been no quarrel between the two disciplines. But in fact Pythagorean mathematics, and the mathematics of the Academy, were substitutes for physical investigation. Geometry had usurped the place of physics. In the Platonic system spatial relations were reality. The true science was *a priori* science. The only cosmology to which it could lead was the cosmology of the *Timaeus*. The Garden had to defend science against such a deformation. Atomism and Pythagorean mathematics are incompatible. The non-mathematical, purely physical conception, of the atom, that is to say a body spatially extended and therefore mathematically divisible, but in fact physically indivisible—this concept was fundamental for physics and therefore fundamental for Epicurus. But it was a deduction from sense-evidence, not a truth "remembered" by the soul by sheltering itself from contact with material things. The dispute, therefore, as to the priority of reason or experience, mathematics or natural philosophy, goes to the roots of the difference between Platonism and Epicureanism. It is surely an odd proof of ignorance and indifference in Epicurus to the higher things of the mind that he should have succeeded in converting one of the most distinguished mathematicians of the day to his point of view. One would suppose it was evidence rather of the likelihood, which there is now documentary material to support, that Epicurus had addressed himself seriously to the study of the fundamental differences between his own philosophy and that of the Academy, and was able to impress a trained mathematician with the justice of his views.

Of course I do not intend by this to maintain that Epicurus himself was a good mathematician. There is no evidence that he was, and something, at least, to suggest that he was not. He would seem in this case to have emptied the baby out with the bath. Concerned to defend the domain of physics from the encroachments of a brand of mathematics that came not to assist it but to oust it, he seems to have failed to appreciate the true service mathematics could render to the cause of natural philosophy. He made every effort to observe, none to measure, events. This defect produced startling results in the sphere of astronomy. Pythagorean mathematics had invaded astronomy with disastrous results of one kind. While making possible an attempt at the estimation of the distances and sizes of the heavenly bodies, it accepted the notion of their eternity

and divinity, and linked these superstitions up with a belief
that all heavenly bodies are perfect spheres and move for
ever in perfect circles. To the Epicurean the heavenly
bodies were chance assemblages of atoms, inanimate,
perishable, and likely to exhibit irregularity of shape and
behaviour. Resisting the Platonic deification of the heavenly
bodies, and suspicious of the mathematical discipline so
intimately linked with these superstitions, Epicurus relied,
for his opinion on the size of the heavenly bodies, purely
on the evidence of his senses unaided by any mathematical
technique.

This led him into one grotesque error. He asserted the
view that the sun is about as big as it appears to us to be.
This is, perhaps, the most damaging proof that can be
brought against him whether of ignorance, or of indifference
to a then existing science. But it is very pertinent to observe
the argument with which Epicurus supported his view.
He pointed out that a fire on earth generally looks much
about the same size so long as one remains near enough
to it to be affected by its heat. But we are still power-
fully affected by the heat of the sun; it is probable therefore
that we are not so far from it as to make it appear much
smaller than it really is. The error is grotesque; but does
not the argument contain the means of its own correction?
If we link it up with the explicit injunction of Epicurus
that every judgment is to be confirmed by reference to
the data of sense-evidence, we see that the error does not
preclude the possibility of future advance. Would that the
same were true of Plato's views! Plato had "proved" that
the sun and moon are divine because we see both Greeks
and barbarians prostrating themselves before them at their
risings and settings. He had proposed to impose these beliefs
as an orthodoxy, and to maintain them by an inquisition

dealing out punishments of imprisonment and death to honest disbelievers. It is a strange comment on our civilization that Plato should be looked upon as the crown of Greek wisdom, and Epicurus despised as an indolent spirit in a decadent age who could not bestir his limp soul to scale the Platonic heights.

We have spoken of the opposition between the Epicurean and Platonic systems on epistemology and mathematics. It remains to say a word or two on another closely connected subject, the theory of the nature of language. In his *History of the Inductive Sciences* (vol. i, p. 27), Whewell writes: "There are two ways of comprehending nature, the one by examining words only and the thoughts which they call up; the other by attending to the facts and things which bring these notions into being. . . . The Greeks followed the former, the *verbal* or *notional* course, and failed." Now Whewell is wrong in levelling this charge against the Greeks; he ought to have confined his attack to certain of the Greek schools, particularly the school of Plato, and to have exempted certain of the schools, particularly that of Epicurus.

Plato did not understand the nature of language, as a study of the *Cratylus* makes clear. He did not clearly understand the symbolic nature of words, but thought that there was some essential connexion between the word and thing symbolized. He was thus at the mercy of words. Of this we have had a notable example in his analysis of motion. Having decided that his strange concept of a "motion that moves itself" can properly be called Soul or Psyche, he straightway endows the "motion that moves itself" with all the rich content of the word Soul;[7] and since the heavenly bodies appear to move themselves he endows them with thought and feeling and generally all the phenomena of life.

The Ionian philosophers had been quite free of this confusion, but since it had been established in philosophy by Plato it had to be formally removed by Epicurus. He therefore teaches that language is a natural phenomenon like another, explicable only by attention to its history. Roughly the history of language, according to him, is that vocal sounds forced from men under the stress of emotion, as they are from other animals, were developed by convention into a device for conveying thoughts from one man to another. Accordingly if you wish to use language as an aid to the investigation of Nature you must always be careful to determine the meaning of words by reference to things, not the nature of things by an examination of words.[8]

The emphasis laid by Epicurus on the identification of philosophy with a knowledge of Nature, and on sense-evidence as the criterion of truth, brought his school into close contact with the Hippocratic doctors who had similar aims and views. The frequent employment of technical Epicurean terminology in the medical treatises of the age, of which an example has been quoted on page 63, is proof of the influence of his school on the progress of medical science. Epicurus himself wrote on the subject. Medicine was taught in the Epicurean school at Naples which Virgil frequented as a youth. The De Rerum Natura is rich in physiological material. And, of course, the Epicurean doctrine of the mortality of the soul is as securely based on physiological evidence as the Platonic view of its immortality is, insecurely, on mathematics.

Epicureans, owing to their quarrel with the mathematicians, did not play a part in the advance of astronomical studies that took place at this time, except in the very important sense that one of the main features of their programme of popular enlightenment was the attack on the astral theology which Plato advocated in the *Laws* and which played a large part in Stoicism. The association of psychic activities with lumps of inanimate matter was for Epicurus the ruin both of science and religion. As we learn from Lucretius,[9] the Epicureans thought the sun and moon much fitter to afford examples of things "quite without vital motion and sense" than to be numbered among the gods; and, true to their physiological views, they pointed out the absurdity of supposing mind to exist without the appropriate physical structure, "far away from the sinews and the blood." In the strength of these convictions the main weight of the Epicurean attack on superstition was directed against the astral theology of Plato and the Stoics. In the *Letter to Herodotus* Epicurus speaks on this point as follows:

"The motions of the heavenly bodies, and their turnings and eclipses and risings and settings, and kindred phenomena to these, must not be thought to be due to any being who controls and ordains or has ordained them and at the same time enjoys perfect bliss together with immortality. For trouble and care and anger and favours are not consistent with a life of blessedness, but these things come to pass where there is weakness and fear and dependence on neighbours. Nor again must we believe that the heavenly bodies, which are but fire agglomerated in a mass, possess blessedness while voluntarily taking upon themselves these movements. Rather must we preserve the majestic significance of all expressions, such as blessedness, which we apply to our conceptions of the gods, in order that there may not arise out of them opinions contrary to the notion of their majesty. Otherwise this very contradiction will cause the greatest disturbance in men's souls. Therefore we must believe that it is due to the original inclusion of matter in such agglomerations during the birth-process of the world that this law of regular succession is also brought about."[10]

It is usual to regard the attack of Epicurus in this passage as being directed against "popular mythology."[11] This view seems without foundation. "The phenomena of the heavens are always adduced," writes Nilsson, "as a main source of the belief in gods. *But this belief is not of popular origin.* Of the Greek natural sciences astronomy was that which had developed farthest and was studied most eagerly; this is the true reason why the heavenly bodies became involved in the discussion of religious and scientific questions and occupied a prominent place therein. Their cult only attained popular significance when astrology under Oriental influence pressed forward into a position of prominence; *philosophy had prepared the way by impressing upon the mind of the public, and more particularly the educated public, the idea of the special claim of the heavenly bodies to divinity.*"[12] For "philosophy" in the italicized portion at the end of this passage read "Plato," especially the Plato of the *Laws*, and we shall have run to earth the special object of Epicurus's attack.

For, in spite of the general agreement that popular mythology is the villain of the piece, is it conceivable that Epicurus had not Plato here in mind? Assuredly his attack is such as to embrace popular mythology; but it seems also to envisage some precise formulation of an astral theology by an educated mind, or minds. The manual called the *Letter to Herodotus* is itself addressed to trained and cultivated minds who could not be unfamiliar with the main currents of thought in their day, and if Epicurus confined himself to attacking popular mythology, he would fail to resolve the doubts of those familiar with the Platonic and Stoic doctrine on celestial phenomena. And in point of fact the theories he attacks involve a closer attention to formal astronomical studies than is compatible with popular mythology. This theological interpretation which he rejects of "the motions of the heavenly bodies and their turnings (i.e. the solstices and the more complicated behaviour of the planets) and eclipses and risings and settings and kindred phenomena to these" does not smack of popular mythology but of a sophisticated theory of the divine order. And in particular the reference to the "law of regular succession," and the rejection of the argument for the divinity of the heavenly bodies based on it, seem to make it clear that Epicurus had more than popular mythology in mind in making his attack. It is my contention that the attack is directed, not against popular mythology in itself, but against the educated versions of popular mythology sponsored by such philosophers as Plato and the Stoics. The point is of fundamental importance for the understanding of the whole orientation of the Epicurean movement. It was the whole system of the Golden Man from its false metaphysical origins to its stultifying political conclusions which Epicurus sought to overthrow, as the essential preliminary to the rescue of the human mind from the incubus of superstition.

[1] *Diogenes Laertius*, ed. R. D. Hicks (Loeb Library), vol. ii, p. 356.
[2] A. W. Benn, *The Greek Philosophers*, 2nd ed., 1914, p. 230.
[3] A. E. Taylor, *Plato*, 1926, p. 463.
[4] Diogenes Laertius, *Epicurus*, par. 37.

⁵ The opinion of Bignone (*L'Aristotele perduto e la formazione philo-sophica di Epicuro*, Firenze, 1936) that Epicurus had much enriched the tradition of Atomism by his defence of it against the positions of the Platonic and Peripatetic schools, is confirmed by the latest researches. See Wolfgang Schmidt, *Epikurs Kritik der platonischen Elementenlehre*, Leipzig, 1938, p. 55: "Obschon nun Epikur Platon nicht richtig beurteilt und beurteilen kann, hat er doch eine beachtliche Leistung vollbracht: der behandelte Text ist eine anschauliche Illustration der Tatsache, dass Epikur nicht nur Lebens-philosoph und religioser Prophet war, sondern auch als theoreticher Denker eine nicht unbedeutende geistesgeschtliche Aufgabe zu lösen hatte: den Atomismus in Kampf und Auseinander-setzung mit Theorien anderer Herkunft aufrecht zu erhalten."

Attention may be directed also to the admirably argued paragraphs in A. H. Armstrong's article on "The Gods in Plato, Plotinus, Epicurus," the *Classical Quarterly*, July-October, 1938, pp. 191, 192. Here Epicurus's tripartite division of events into those caused by necessity, those caused by chance, and those within our control, is considered in relation to the Platonic and Aristotelian background. "We see that what Epicurus has done, and he seems to have been original in doing it, is to split the traditional conception of Chance-Necessity so that, while remaining strictly within the bounds of his system and involving no principle of explanation which is immaterial or possessed of reason, he provides himself with a framework or background of regularity and order while leaving room for an erratic, capricious principle in the world. . . . It is tempting to recognize in this distinction a conscious attempt to provide an adequate substitute for the Platonic cosmology, on a materialistic basis."

⁶ Cicero, *De Natura Deorum*, i, 12.

⁷ *Laws*, x, 896. ΚΛ. Τὸ ἑαυτὸ κινεῖν φῂς λόγον ἔχειν τὴν αὐτὴν οὐσίαν, ἥνπερ τοὔνομα ὃ δὴ πάντες ψυχὴν προσαγο-ρεύομεν; ΑΘ. Φημί γε.

⁸ See *Letter to Herodotus*, pars. 75, 76, and 37, 38. The few words I have devoted to the Epicurean theory of language in the text give no idea of the elegance and elaboration of their work in this department. See Philip H. de Lacy, "The Epicurean Analysis of Language" (*American Journal of Philology*, Janaury 1939). This able and well-documented survey of the present state of our knowledge in this particular is one more proof of the revolution in the understanding of Epicureanism that modern scholarship has achieved.

⁹ Lucretius, *De Rerum Natura*, v, 110 ff.

¹⁰ Epicurus, *Letter to Herodotus*, pars. 76, 77. The translation is that of Cyril Bailey, with a few slight modifications of expression.

¹¹ Bailey in his note on this passage refers to the opinions rejected by Epicurus as "the false explanations of popular mythology."

¹² Nilsson, *op. cit.*, p. 267.

CHAPTER TWELVE

THE RELIGION OF EPICURUS

Determinism and Free-will. The Gods of the People. The New Theology of Epicurus.

It was not the intention of Epicurus, if he could rescue the Greek world from the influence of the Academy, to restore the physical system of Democritus without change. The atomic system, as constituted by Leucippus and Democritus, suffered, in his eyes, from a fundamental defect; it established a doctrine of universal determinism, including man in the same chain of mechanical causation as inanimate matter. This doctrine of mechanical determinism was, in the eyes of Epicurus, a worse incubus on the human race than a belief in the myths.

In the view of Epicurus the freedom of the human will was a matter of fact established by observation. Man does not simply move because he is pushed. He makes up his mind to move, and then puts the intention into effect. And the motives that determine his action may be infinitely various, from a desire to get something to eat to a desire to rescue the human mind from superstition. A properly trained man would always be guided in his actions by the philosophy of Nature so far as it is understood. Such philosophy might include the most altruistic motives. "Vain is the word of a philosopher that heals no suffering of man."

But how are such opinions and sentiments to be reconciled with the doctrine of atomism? If the universe is merely a pattern of atoms in the void, where is the room for such

148

idealistic developments as those defended by Epicurus? The answer of Epicurus was that such things as beauty, truth, and goodness are as much a part of Nature as anything else. He did not deny their existence. What he did deny was the possibility of their existing in some immaterial world where immaterial souls also exist before and after they come into this one. That to Epicurus was nonsense. But that men should be animated by great ideals, that they should love another more than themselves, that they could find their happiness in devotion to impersonal causes, such as the study of Nature or the organization of a movement for the rescue of the human mind from superstition—these ideas were not only not strange to Epicurus, they were the very breath of his nostrils.

It followed, then, that if the universe in its ultimate analysis is but atoms and void, the atoms had to be of such a kind, or at least capable of such arrangement, as to admit of these future developments. In the writings of Epicurus we find that he endowed the atoms with an element of spontaneity in movement, and that he connected this with the phenomenon of the freedom of the will in man. In the writings of his disciple, Lucretius, much is made of the infinite possibilities that may result from fresh arrangements of atoms.[1] It is always dangerous to compare the opinions of ancient thinkers with the results of modern science. But if we bear clearly in mind that the whole science of chemistry as it exists to-day was still to be discovered, there can then be no danger, and there is much illumination, in comparing the doctrine of the Epicureans on the new qualities that come into existence as a result of new patterns of arrangement in the atoms, to the modern realization of the fact that there is no single constituent in the human body that does not also exist in an inorganic state. The same elements that make up inanimate bodies, which may have powers of cohesion, attraction, surface tension, and so on, may also make up plants, which are sensitive and can grow and reproduce themselves; and animals, which can, in addition, move and exercise certain mental powers; and men, who may aspire to philosophy. Within the limits of their ignorance of the sciences of the modern world this general idea was quite clear to the Epicureans. Like the old Ionian thinkers they were evolutionists. But they had carried their thinking further, and they looked upon freedom of the will as a quality of matter organized in a certain way, a quality which had come into existence in the course of the history of the world we inhabit, and the nature and limitations of which could therefore only be understood by the study of that comprehensive subject, Natural Philosophy. It was in the pursuit of such enquiry that they struck out such admirable theories as that on the origin and development of language to which we have referred; and in the pursuit of it they also created the science of anthropology, of which more anon.[2]

It is commonly said of the doctrine of the *clinamen* or *swerve* in the atoms, by which Epicurus endeavoured to supply the atom with an element of spontaneity, that it is a puerile invention, sufficient in itself to prove his philosophical incompetence. It is further said that he borrowed all that was good in atomism from Democritus, and that in addition to spoiling the conception by this modification, he showed his ingratitude by his claim to be independent of Democritus in his fundamental conceptions, and by belittling his achievement. Happily the writings of Cyril Bailey and others in modern times have gone far to modify these harsh judgments.

In the opinion of the present writer, though it is often

said that Epicurus stole the atomic system of Democritus in unexamined haste because it suited his corrupt ethical theories, and spoiled in stealing it, the atomism of Democritus both cried out for the correction introduced by Epicurus, and was wholly unfitted to be incorporated in the brilliant system of Epicureanism until the correction had been made. Epicurus adopted atomism because it was the most assured result of the two hundred years of physical speculation that separated Thales from Democritus. But he knew that the doctrine of the nature of the atoms was lacking in the confirmation of sense-experience. In the nature of things the atoms can never be the subject of sense-experience, though they are the foundation of a system in which the criterion of truth is the evidence of the senses. The theory of the atom must, therefore, according to the system of Epicurus, be always liable to revision if experience should bring to light any new knowledge concerning sensible objects inconsistent with the theory of the nature of the atom as constituted at any time. Sense-evidence is not based on the theory of the atom; the theory of the atom is based on sense-experience. Now it was the opinion of Epicurus that one important element in the behaviour of some of the things we see and touch had been overlooked by Democritus, namely that element in living things by which they differ from inanimate matter, and which we call free-will. In the view of Epicurus the Democritean theory of the atom had been erected on an insufficient foundation of observation. The necessary correction was made by the introduction of the doctrine of the swerve.

Since there has been so much belittling of Epicurus, and so much adulation of Plato, it is well that one, in comparing them, should state his opinions without equivocation. In my view, then, the derided doctrine of the atomic swerve is far superior logic and far superior philosophy and far superior science to the tissue of illogicalities by which Plato seeks to establish the conclusion that the sun can think and feel and plan. It is clean, honest thinking which can only help any other enquirer who aspires to do better. And Epicurus felt no necessity to imprison and execute those who did not see their way to agree with him.

In the passage from the *Letter to Herodotus* quoted on page 143 it will have been observed that Epicurus rejected the Platonic view that the heavenly bodies are animated deities, not only in the interest of a true view of the nature of the heavenly bodies, but more explicitly in the interests of a true view of the gods. What, then, we must ask was the Epicurean theology? This is a vexed question, on which, fortunately, fresh light has recently been shed.

Though some ancient writers charged Epicurus with being an atheist—the accusation is made by Cicero and Plutarch—it has always been known that he professed belief in the gods, and that he attached great importance to them in his system. They were objects of reverence and devotion, and afforded an example to the pious of what the true Epicurean life ought to be. But it was not clear how the existence of immortal gods could be accounted for on the basis of the atomic system. Furthermore, Epicurus insisted that his gods took no part in the management of the universe; and he was supposed to have taught that they took no interest in men. He located them in the *intermundia*, or empty regions of space between the countless worlds in the existence of which he believed. They appeared to be superfluous adjuncts to the Epicurean universe. And the wonder was why Epicurus should have troubled to include them, unless, indeed, the suspicion of Plutarch were true, that he had done so merely in order to escape prosecution for atheism. It seems possible to understand the matter somewhat more clearly in the light of recent research.

To a sympathetic student of Epicureanism it had always proved possible to find something to say in justification of the Epicurean theology. Thus Gassendi, in the seventeenth century, had maintained that Epicurus had taught a singularly pure religion. He drew a distinction between the servile and filial elements in religion, the servile being those concerned with an interchange of services between men and gods, the filial those concerned with pure devotion offered by man to god, and pointed out that it was only in the servile element that the religion of Epicurus was lacking. There was justification for Gassendi's plea, but it did little to integrate the religion of Epicurus with his general scheme of things. It proved his piety, but not his intellectual competence.

In modern times apologists for religion have attached enormous importance to the argument for the existence of God derived from the supposed universal consent of all peoples. In the *De Natura Deorum* of Cicero (i, 16), the defender of Epicureanism is made to remark of the founder of the school: *Solus enim vidit primum esse deos, quod in omnium animis eorum notionem impressisset ipsa natura* (He alone saw that the first proof of the existence of gods is that Nature herself has impressed the idea of them on the minds of all men). Martha in modern times pointed out how remarkable it was that Epicurus should have been the first to employ this argument; and others also have drawn attention to it. The point is of importance to us as an indication of the intimate connexion of the Epicurean theology with the rest of the system. Epicurus did not believe that any notion could exist in the mind which had not resulted from images impressed upon the organs of sense; and these images, he thought, were conveyed to the senses by streams of atoms from the object perceived. If, then, notions of the gods are commonly found in men's minds, they must have got there because there actually do exist gods who have given off the images that have produced these notions.

There has never been any people so prone to anthropomorphism as the Greeks. At least from the time of Homer onwards, the Greeks, apart from a few philosophers, always conceived of their gods as being made in the likeness of man. It was in these gods of the people that Epicurus believed, though he did not believe all that the people believed about them. His theology is a sort of reformed popular theology. It is in the second paragraph of his Letter to Menoeceus that we get our fullest information on his views:

"The things which I used unceasingly to commend to you, these do and practice, considering them to be the first principles of the good life. First of all believe that god is a being immortal and blessed, even as the common idea of a god is engraved on men's minds, and do not assign to him anything alien to his immortality or ill-suited to his blessedness: but believe about him everything that can uphold his blessedness and immortality. For gods there are, since the knowledge of them is by clear vision. But they are not such as the many believe them to be: for indeed they do not consistently represent them as they believe them to be. And the impious man is not he who denies the gods of the many, but he who attaches to the gods the beliefs of the many."

In the passage we quoted on page 143, in which Epicurus attacked the idea of the divinity of the heavenly bodies, there was no reference to the beliefs of the many, for the very good reason that the astral theology which Epicurus there attacked was not the creed of the populace, but the teaching of the schools. The religion which Epicurus rejected was the consciously constructed state-religion of the political philosophers. But now when we come to the religion which Epicurus accepts but desires to reform, we find that it is the religion of the people. His disciple is urged to believe in the immortality and blessedness of god, "even as the common idea of a god is engraved on men's minds."

The contrast is striking, and is in keeping with our interpretation of the whole orientation of the Epicurean movement. Epicureanism, though of course it depended on its brilliant leader, was a popular movement. It was a movement to rally the courage and self-respect of the little people, of the average man. Critias (see page 88) had spoken of the "shrewd and wise-thoughted man," who had invented the idea of an eternal, all-seeing deity, and had placed his gods in the vault of heaven and connected them with the lightning and the thunderbolt *because he thought that this would be the best way to frighten men.* In Pindar's poetry these gods had been the friends and protectors of princes and potentates, and had thundered and lightened in a way very consoling to these great persons (who were, after all, the products of the extra-marital intrigues of their divine protectors) and in a way very terrifying to obscure people who hadn't a god among their ancestors. Plato had refurbished and refined the whole conception to suit a sophisticated age and the moral sensibilities of his own complex character; but he was so remote from any feeling of sympathy with the people or understanding of them, that he never thought except in terms of legislation, and the imposition of regulations from above; his degree of faith in the attractive powers of his astral theology is indicated by his realization that it would need to be imposed by the police and maintained by persecution. It was this consciously constructed, state-imposed religion of fear that was the special object of the attack of Epicurus. And when he was dubbed "atheist" by Plutarch and others, it was because they could not or would not distinguish between this state-religion and simple belief in the gods.

Plutarch, in his extant polemic against the Epicurean Colotes, writes as follows (I quote the lively old version of Philemon Holland): "Religion it is that constraineth and holdeth together all humane society, this is the foundation, prop, and stay of all Laws, which the Epicureans subvert and overthrow directly, who go not round about the bush, as they say, not secretly and by circuit of covert speeches, but openly and even at the first assault set upon the principal point of all, to wit, the opinion of God and Religion." This is evidence both of the boldness of the Epicurean attack, and of its object, to wit, the religion that was devised to buttress the law. It was only in this sense of religion that Plutarch had any grounds for calling Epicurus atheist.

But, in view of his stark hostility to political religion, it is of great interest to find that Epicurus felt that there was a genuine popular religion in existence, not necessarily alien to his philosophy, to which he could appeal. His adherents were to believe in blessed and immortal deities, like the common idea of a god that is engraved on men's minds. But, continues Epicurus, there are inconsistencies in the popular conception, and these must be weeded out. The inconsistencies he explains in the sentences that follow on the passage we have just quoted. It is of interest as an indication of the important progress that is still being made in the understanding of Epicureanism that the correct interpretation of these sentences should only have been achieved within the last few years.[3]

The error of the popular view of the gods, according to Epicurus, is the belief that the gods either punish wicked men, or (still more grievous error) confer benefits upon them. In fact the gods, while they "welcome" good men, that is men like themselves, are indifferent to bad men. The reason for this distinction between the attitude of the gods to good and bad men is this, that good men have no disorderly wishes which they expect the gods to execute nor do they act in a way to disturb the divine peace.[4] But bad men are constantly devising evil, praying for the destruction of one another, seeking for material advantages or forgiveness for their sins by offering sacrifices, and generally acting in such a way that communion with them is inconsistent with such peace and blessedness as we must associate with the conception of the divine nature. Good men have never anything to fear from the gods; on the contrary, by devotion to them they may hope to enjoy during the brief span of their mortal lives communion in their immortal felicity. Neither have bad men anything to fear from the gods, except the pain of separation from them, if they should be capable of feeling it, and the mental disturbance which their false conceptions of the deity can engender.

Such, in outline, was the Epicurean effort to reform the popular theology. It has some remarkable features. Its basis in the supposed universality of "visions" of the anthropomorphic deities of Greek mythology, which are accepted as certain proof of the real existence of the divine beings who, in accordance with Epicurean theories of vision, must be supposed to be the source of them, is desperately insecure. But is it any less secure than the modern

version of the same argument for the existence of God?
It costs me some effort of imagination to understand how
Epicurus could hold to this opinion. It costs me an equal
effort to understand how, for example, M. Jacques Maritain
can hold to his. "The most reliable inductions of history,"
he tells us, "combine with the conclusions of theology to
prove the existence of a *primitive tradition*, common to the
different branches of the human race and going back to
the origin of mankind. And even in default of any positive
sources of information, it is a very reasonable conjecture
that the first man received from God knowledge together
with existence, that by education he might complete the
work of procreation."[5] Indeed I think that, in spite of my
deep admiration for the intelligence, intellectual integrity,
scholarship, and moral courage of M. Maritain, I find his
opinion more difficult than that of Epicurus, and the
conceptions of anthropology that necessarily devolve from
it less valid, for all the centuries that have passed since then,
than those taught in the Garden in Athens.

If we pass from consideration of the justification of the
Epicurean theology to consideration of its bearing on his
system as a whole, we are struck by two things. In the first
place, while maintaining belief in gods, Epicurus has
banished them from any control of the physical world. He
had faith, but not a faith that could move mountains. This
removes the source of friction between religion and science
that has proved an embarrassment for modern thought. In
the second place, the influence of his gods on men is purely
moral. His gods hold out no rewards or punishments for
men in this world, and Epicurus did not believe in the
next. Epicureans were taught to strain towards their gods
with devotion and love, and to expect that if they kept
their hearts pure the holy images that streamed from the

bodies of the gods would enter freely into their minds carrying with them something of the divine peace and bliss.[6] It was a religion without fear, a religion without miracles, a religion without offerings other than that of a pure heart, based on the traditional beliefs of the people, not necessarily requiring temples or a priesthood, but demanding only a quiet mind. The Epicureans were a sort of Society of Friends with a system of Natural Philosophy as its intellectual core.

[1] *De Rerum Natura*, i, 684–689, 798–802, 817–829.

[2] For the Epicurean notion of the progress of man in history towards freedom from necessity see *Letter to Herodotus*, par. 75: "Moreover, we must suppose that human nature too was taught and constrained to do many things of every kind merely by circumstances; and that later on reasoning elaborated what had been suggested by nature and made further inventions, etc." Thus Purpose makes its appearance in the course of history. It is not a metaphysical, but an historically acquired, character of man.

[3] The universal tradition that Epicurus taught the indifference of the gods to men has been disproved by the success of Christian Jensen in reconstructing from the Herculanean fragments a new letter of Epicurus. It is now clear that what Epicurus taught was the indifference of the gods to *bad* men, but their active friendliness to good. See Christian Jensen, *Ein neuer Brief Epikurs*, Berlin, 1933. A fuller account of Jensen's discovery is given in my own article, "The Gods of Epicurus and the Roman State" (*The Modern Quarterly*, vol. i, No. 3).

[4] Cf. *Fragment LXXIX*: "The man who has attained to peace of mind (ὁ ἀτάραχος) does not cause disturbance to himself or anybody else."

[5] Jacques Maritain, *An Introduction to Philosophy*, Sheed and Ward, p. 24.

[6] See Lucretius, *De Rerum Natura*, vi, 75–78.

CHAPTER THIRTEEN

EPICUREANISM REACHES ROME

Epicureanism abolishes the police function of religion. Greek efforts to restore the impressiveness of the Cults. Polybius finds the Roman Senate supreme in the exploitation of religion for political ends. Epicurean philosophers expelled by the Roman Senate.

One effect of the Epicurean system was to abolish totally the police function of religion. The religion which saw in the lightning, the thunder, earthquake, storm, and disease manifestations of the wrath of offended deities was dismissed as superstition. The fear of suffering after death was dispelled by the doctrine of the mortality of the soul. And the reformed popular religion recommended by Epicurus explicitly taught that the gods do not concern themselves for good or ill with bad men.

It would be interesting to know the extent to which his system had influenced ancient society. An accurate answer is impossible, but that its influence was very wide is certain. Diogenes Laertius, writing in the early years of the third century of our era, speaks of the statues with which his native land honoured Epicurus, and of his friends "so numerous that they could hardly be counted by whole cities." The precise meaning of this enthusiastic compliment is not clear. But it is clear that groups of adherents soon came into existence all over the Greek-speaking world; and we know that they were organized, and that systematic instruction was supplied. In one of the extant fragments from his writings we find Epicurus exclaiming: "Friendship goes dancing round the inhabited world summoning us all to awake and share in the Blessed Life." Friendship and the Blessed Life are technical terms in the movement; the sentence reads like a jubilant cry at the spread of the sect.

The phrase "the inhabited world," too, may engage our attention for a moment. It serves to remind us that the sphere in which Epicurus hoped to operate was no longer confined to his native city, but was coextensive with civilization. The third century was not a happy one for the Greek world, but at least there was a growing sense of the unity of mankind. The reasons for the unhappiness of the Greek world at this time have been brilliantly analysed by Tarn.[1] Briefly, the gulf between rich and poor had widened, and the fear of revolution haunted society. This fear was an old one; but, whereas in the days of the independent city-state each city had more or less conducted its own revolutions and counter-revolutions, now, with the growing unity of the Greek world, revolution and counter-revolution tend to become ecumenical. A threat to the rich in one city is felt to be a threat to all. The Greek States begin to explore the possibility of federal government, and an essential feature of the various Leagues that now begin to dominate the political scene is the proviso that the whole force of any League shall come to the help of a city that is threatened with internal revolution. After the socialist revolution in Sparta effected by King Cleomenes, the Macedonian monarch Antigonus formed a new league explicitly to attack, not Sparta, but the revolution.

It was a society thus torn by civil strife that began to be permeated by the Epicurean movement. And it was such a society that Epicureanism taught men to renounce. If Epicurus called on men to " Free themselves from the prison of business and politics," it was not an invitation to a paradise of *dolce far niente*. He called them out of a ruined world in which "rest was stagnation and activity madness" into an effort to make a better. "Most men," he taught, "fear frugality, and through their fear are led to actions most likely to produce fear." "By means of occupations worthy of a beast abundance of riches is heaped up, but a miserable life results." At the root of civic ambition lay the fear of the jungle. Haunted by fear men trampled each other down. "Men wish to become famous and conspicuous, because they think that they will thus win safety for themselves from other men." But "he who has learned the limits of life knows that that which removes the pain due to want and makes the whole of life complete is easy to obtain; so that there is no need of actions which involve competition." "Of all the things which wisdom acquires to produce the blessedness of the complete life, far the greatest is the possession of friendship." Organize yourselves, then, for the study of Nature and the practice of friendship, and human life will approximate to the divine.

It is understandable that a programme of this sort should have appealed to a distracted society such as we have been describing, and have secured a numerous following. It is less obvious why it should have produced hostility, as it did, among the governing class. Epicurus was not proposing cancellation of debts, redivision of land, or a revolt among the slaves. So far as the evidence goes he was not a revolutionary. The basic question of production does not seem to have occupied his mind. He was not proposing that the distinction between rulers and workers should be abolished, and that all should be compelled to take a hand in productive work. He thought that there would easily be enough for all, if men only understood how modest are their real needs. He was a prophet of the simple life, naïve and innocent in the sphere of political theory. Why, then, should governing circles have frowned upon the movement he initiated?

The answer would appear to be that, in the society we have described, that is to say a society torn by civil strife, governing circles in general took the opposite view to that urged by Epicurus on the question of the religious enlightenment of the masses. While to Epicurus it appeared that the minds of men could never be at rest while they were stuffed with false notions on the nature of things, to the rich oligarchs it appeared that society, that is to say the political system under which they enjoyed their privileges, could never be safe unless they continued to apply the policy of the Noble Lie. While Epicurus and his disciples were busy disseminating a view of things which had deprived religion of every vestige of value as an instrument of political domination, the princes and potentates were becoming increasingly aware that never more than now had society needed a religion that would inspire in the dispossessed a wholesome fear of meddling with the constitution of things. Efforts were made, as Nilsson has pointed out, to increase the impressiveness of religious performances by external means. In the matter of lighting, the old-fashioned torches were replaced by a multitude of lamps. In the Dionysiac mysteries the solemn tones of the water-organ prepared the celebrants for the awakening of the god. The Platonic and Stoic astral gods began to invade the traditional festivals, investing them with a new awe. The priestly knowledge traditional in the aristocratic families was written down, collected, systematized, and adapted to fresh use. Those equipped with this sacral knowledge constituted a new profession. Timotheus, a member of the ancient priestly family of the Eumolpidae, who had charge of the Eleusinian

Mysteries, became, in the phrase of Nilsson, "a kind of minister of public worship to Ptolemy I, helping him to found a branch of the Eleusinian cult and to establish the cult of the new national god, Serapis." These are instances of the widespread activities of those in authority in establishing new cults, or bringing old ones up to date. Such activities as these are not properly described as "popular superstition"; and it was in so far as their rationalist propaganda came into conflict with these aristocratic and governmental religious activities that the Epicureans came to be suspect in the eyes of the authorities.

These considerations all imply a conflict between the religion of the *polis* and the scientific renaissance of Ionia which explains the arrest in the development of Greek science. The Greek city-state has been, perhaps, over-praised in one particular. It is claimed that the ideal of the city-state, which identified the man with the citizen, produced a type of human excellence unknown in the world before. There is a measure of truth in this. But I would urge that where the identity of man and citizen was complete, as in Sparta, culture stagnated; that in Athens the Ionian enlightenment and the constitution of the city-state proved increasingly incompatible; that the Ionian tradition could only be revived by Epicurus because the city-state had degenerated and he withdrew himself from it; and that the reason for the incompatibility of the city-state with Ionian science lay in the unjust social organization of the State. In a city-state, where striking inequalities of wealth prevailed and where in consequence civil war was endemic and often violent, the religion of the State tended more and more to be transformed by the ruling-class into an instrument of mental oppression utterly incompatible with the spread of enlightenment. This was the main reason for the slow strangulation of the great speculative movement of natural philosophy that began in Ionia in the sixth century, flourished for about two hundred years, and then slowly died for about another eight centuries. The other main reason for the decay of Greek science, not discussed in this book, was its divorce from the productive activities of life which resulted from the prevalence of a slave economy. Both these causes for the ultimate failure of the great scientific movement of Greece have their roots deep in society.

Epicurus died in 270 B.C. We cannot be sure when his philosophy first reached Rome. But we do know that within a hundred years of his death the Roman Senate had given evidence of its dislike of it. In the year 173 B.C. the Senate expelled from the city two disciples of Epicurus, Alcaeus and Philiscus, for "introducing pleasures."[2] Significant of the spread of the propagandist activities of the sect is the fact that while in the West we have this first evidence of conflict between Epicureanism and the great centre of government in the Italian peninsula, in the East, in Antioch, that strange monarch Antiochus Epiphanes is said to have been converted to the Epicurean view. Here again we are dependent upon the recent interpretation of a fragment of papyrus for this remarkable information. From it we learn that the Epicurean Philonides went to the Syrian court, accompanied by a large body of literary men, for the express purpose of securing this important convert. "After Antiochus had been plied with a battery of no less than *one hundred and twenty-five tracts* he succumbed." The great influence which Philonides thus acquired he endeavoured to use to promote humanitarian ends.[3]

The action of the Roman Senate is an important clue to the character of Epicureanism as a social force at this time. The wisdom of the Roman Fathers is proverbial, and their adverse judgment on the new philosophy, if we could understand its motive, should be illuminating for our enquiry. Unfortunately, though the political wisdom of the Roman government at this epoch was great, neither the literary culture of the city nor its political condition was such that questions of social policy became matters of literary polemic or public discussion, as they did in the democracy of Athens. We have therefore no philosophical dialogue, scientific essay, or tragic drama from Roman sources which might supply the deficiency in our information. Nor are there many who will feel that the whole mind of the Senate has been revealed to posterity in the brief tradition that the philosophers were expelled for "introducing pleasures." It is doubly fortunate, therefore, that we should possess from an outside source of unique authority a characterization of the mind and policy of the Roman Senate on that particular problem of contemporary society with which the Epicureans made it their business to meddle.

Six or seven years after the expulsion of the Epicurean philosophers, the Greek statesman Polybius was brought to Rome as a hostage and retained there for seventeen years. Owing to his intellectual eminence he was sought after by the more enlightened of the Roman ruling class, and came to exercise a profound influence on the thought of the most cultured men of the day, particularly those associated with the group known as the Scipionic Circle. He, on his side, was so filled with admiration for Roman ways that he decided to devote his experienced pen to the recording of the story of Roman expansion, thus bringing their history for the first time under the illumination of a sophisticated intellect used to the handling of ideas. Polybius, if not in originality the foremost of Greek historians—we reserve that honour for Thucydides—was certainly foremost in political experience. It will be understood, then, how fortunate we are to possess his judgment on the attitude of the Roman Senate to that problem, which, in the light of what has been the main argument of this book, may be claimed to have been the special concern of Epicureanism.

"I will venture the assertion," wrote Polybius, "that what the rest of mankind deride is the foundation of Roman greatness, namely superstition. This element has been introduced into every aspect of their private and public life, with every artifice to awe the imagination, in a degree which could not be improved upon. Many possibly will be at a loss to understand this: my view is that it has been done to impress the masses. If it were possible to have a State in which all the citizens were philosophers, perhaps we might dispense with this sort of thing. But the masses in every State are unstable, full of lawless desires, of irrational anger, and violent passion. All that can be done, then, is to hold them in check by fears of the unseen and other shams of the same sort. It was not for nothing, but with deliberate design, that the men of old introduced to the masses notions about the gods and views on the after-life. The folly and heedlessness are ours, who seek to dispel such illusions."[4]

If we bear in mind that the one "pleasure" above all others that the Epicureans sought to "introduce" was the freedom of mind that comes from discarding false notions about the gods and views on the after-life, we shall be fully in possession of the motives of the Roman Fathers when they expelled the Epicureans in 173 B.C. for "introducing pleasures."

The main purport of Polybius's statement—that the Roman Senate was successfully carrying out the religious policy we first found clearly defined in Critias, and of which Plato tried to elaborate a variety suited to the exigencies of his own time and place—is clear. But his analysis yields us more information than that. When he says that "the rest of mankind" deride superstition, he must be referring principally, if not exclusively, to the Greeks; and his words are testimony to the progress of popular enlightenment among them.

But there is a further point that emerges from his remarks which seems worthy of a slightly longer discussion. The conscience of Polybius is not wholly at ease under the situation as he has analysed it. "If it were possible," he writes, "to have a State in which all the citizens were philosophers, perhaps we might dispense with this sort of thing." As a historian concerned for the truth Polybius was acutely conscious of the danger to his profession of the habit of the pious fiction. Thus in his Sixteenth Book, chap. 12, he refers to the report that a certain statue of Artemis, though it stood in the open air, was never touched by snow or rain, and continues: "Throughout the whole of my history I find myself somehow in continuous opposition to statements of this sort on the part of historians, and continuously distressed by them. . . . I admit that there are cases in which historians must be pardoned for reporting marvels of this kind in so far as their intention is to maintain the piety of the mob towards the gods; anything that goes beyond this is inexcusable. Perhaps it is not easy in every case to fix the limit; it is not, however, impossible. We must excuse a little ignorance or even a little falsification; but what goes beyond this ought to be rejected in my opinion."

It will be seen that Polybius's solution of his problem is not very impressive; it is not one which a historian would find it very easy to apply in practice. We recall J. M. Robertson's comment on "the fatal maxim of ancient scepticism, that religion is a necessary restraint upon the multitude." This, says Robertson, "brought it about that everywhere, in the last resort, the unenlightened multitude became a restraint upon reason and free thought."[5]

But what in fact are we to think of the plea Polybius here advances in justification of the governmental technique of inculcating superstition? Is it true that "the masses in every State are unstable, full of lawless desires, of irrational anger, and violent passion"? It must be admitted that if this be the irreducible fact then the advocates of the Noble Lie have their justification. But is it the irreducible fact? When Plato formulated, in the *Republic*, this judgment on the masses (for Polybius is only repeating Plato), was it, in fact, an informed judgment on an extremely complex sociological problem or merely a convenient solution of his economic problem? Undoubtedly the latter. His ideal of society implied a ruling class exempt from manual toil and a large class of workers incapable of citizenship. It suited him to suppose, or pretend, that Nature had provided such a class of workers. The refusal of the workers to accept this doctrine was proof to him that they were unstable and full of lawless desires.

This convenient solution of his economic problem was knit by Plato into the very structure of his social philosophy. Virtue for him was not a prerogative of humanity but of a class. "Let me note," he writes, "that the manifold and complex passions and pleasures and pains are generally found in children and women and servants, and in the free-men so called who are of the lowest and more numerous class. Whereas the moderate desires which follow reason, and are under the guidance of mind and true opinion, are to be found only in a few, and those the best born and best educated. These types are represented in our State; but the meaner desires of the many are held down by the virtuous

desires and wisdom of the few."[6] Accordingly he divided
society into a class of governors, who embody its reason;
a class of soldiers and police, who embody its courage; and a
class of workers, who embody—what? Industry? Ingenuity?
Skill? Patience? Or any good thing? No; but lust, greed,
passion, violence! Reason, the distinctive virtue of the
rulers, he situates in the head; courage, the distinctive virtue
of the armed forces, he situates in the breast; and the distinctive virtue of the workers he situates in the belly and the
loins! Such was the social philosophy to which Polybius,
whose sympathies were oligarchic, subscribed. To these
oligarchic sympathies of his, together with the Platonic
ideology which justified them, we owe his enthusiastic
account of the success of the Roman Senate in the maintenance of superstition for reasons of state.

But the words of Polybius also reveal to us that the general
progress of enlightenment in Greece had been such that the
analysis of Plato, with its corollary of government through
superstition, no longer commanded universal intellectual
assent. This progress, in the opinion of Polybius, had been
such as to constitute a real threat to privilege. "The folly and
heedlessness are ours (i.e. the Greeks') who seek to dispel
such illusions." This passage of Polybius, therefore, shows us
Mediterranean civilization at the cross-roads and reveals the
deep-seated contradiction in Greek society which induced
its oligarchic leaders to throw in their lot with Rome. The
progress of enlightenment had reached a pitch at which it
was incompatible with the social organization of the day;
and the achievement of the Romans which the Greeks hailed
with such respect did not consist simply, as history has been
inclined to stress, in sanitation and road-building, but, above
and beyond these engineering triumphs, in the mental
enslavement of the people. The struggle between Ionian

enlightenment and oligarchic society is no longer to be
played out on the tiny stage of individual Greek city-states
but on a vast stage commensurate with the dominion of
Rome. With the spread of Roman power will go not only
roads, sanitation, and taxes, but also their successful technique
for the enslavement of the human mind.

This was the juncture at which Epicureanism had its first
encounter with the Senate at Rome. The Epicureans, as we
have seen, despised the values of the oligarchic State, and
opposed the spread of superstition. They thought the mob
ignorant, but not incapable of enlightenment; indeed to
spread enlightenment was the main purpose of their movement. They did not possess two doctrines, one for a ruling
class and another for the ruled; they had only one doctrine
which they were anxious to spread to all that needed it.
Their movement was not an academic one, aimed exclusively
at correcting errors of thought in rival schools. To correct
such errors was necessary; but they did not separate error
from its social consequences. Lucretius has told us what
prompted Epicurus to his life's work—the spectacle of
human life prostrate under the weight of religion. Is there
need to say more? Is it not clear why the Senate dismissed
the Epicurean philosophers from Rome?

[1] See *The Hellenistic Age*, by Bury, Barber, Bevan, and Tarn,
Cambridge, 1923, pp. 108, 127, 137.

[2] See *Athenaeus*, xii, 547 A. The date of the expulsion is put at
154 B.C. by Altheim (*op. cit.*, p. 332). The point is immaterial to my
argument.

[3] See E. R. Bevan, *The House of Seleucus*, ii, pp. 276, 277.

[4] *Histories*, vi, 56.

[5] *Op. cit.*, vol. i, p. 155.

[6] *Republic*, iii, 431. This is simply the Pindaric conception of oligarchy
and democracy tricked out with a little pseudo-philosophy (cf. p. 80).

CHAPTER FOURTEEN

LUCRETIUS

The intense passion of the poet. The purpose of the poem. The Invocation to Venus. Religio. *The* anti-Lucrèce chez Lucrèce. *The contemporary relevance of the poem. Epicureanism in Italy. Cicero and Lucretius. The Stoics at Rome. Varro and the three-fold classification of religion. Lucretius and the Delphic Oracle.*

All students of Lucretius in every age have been agreed upon one thing, his passionate intensity. He possessed this quality to a degree that it is difficult, if not impossible, to match in any other writer. It is the distinctive thing about him. In common with all other students of his writings I have been conscious of it too. But I find that, while to me this passion and intensity is justified by what he has to say, and is, indeed, the only adequate response to the situation he describes, others find it unaccountable, that is to say, unrelated to the poet's theme, and therefore to be explained in terms of a lack of mental balance. It was the wish to make a comment on the passion of Lucretius that led me to the composition of the present book. It did not seem possible to explain what I consider to be the motive for the *arduus furor* of the poet without an effort to put his poem in a historical context from which it has been divorced by time and circumstance.

It was the opinion of Mommsen that the *De Rerum Natura* was forced out of the poet by the circumstances of his age. "Horror and antipathy towards that terrible world in general, in which and for which the poet wrote, suggested this poem." This is just. But in what else he writes Mommsen seems off the mark. He supposes the object of the poet's attack to have been especially "the wild foreign faiths and superstitions of the multitude." And he deplores the fact that so great a poet should have wasted his time disposing of such childish beliefs by the aid of a dreary philosophical system:

"It is a remarkable fatality, that this man of extraordinary talents, far superior in originality of poetic endowment to most if not to all his contemporaries, fell upon an age in which he felt himself strange and forlorn, and in consequence of this made the most singular mistake in the selection of a subject. The system of Epicurus, which converts the universe into a great vortex of atoms and undertakes to explain the origin and end of the world as well as all the problems of life in a purely mechanical way, was doubtless somewhat less silly than the conversion of myths into history which was attempted by Euhemerus and after him by Ennius; but it was not an ingenious or a fresh system, and the task of poetically unfolding the mechanical view of the world was of such a nature that never probably did poet expend life and art on a more ungrateful theme."

This is to misconceive both the character of Epicureanism and the relation of the poet to his task. In the first place Epicureanism is not a purely mechanical system; it was the specific originality of Epicurus in the domain of physics to have defended freedom of the will in man as a product of evolution.[1] And in the second place Lucretius was not a poet looking for a subject, he was a man with a subject who chose verse as the form in which to present it. Lucretius would be Lucretius if he had written in prose; he would not be Lucretius if he had not expounded Epicureanism.

To speak of him as having made a mistake in the selection of his subject is to destroy all possibility of fruitful criticism. Lucretius *is* the author of the *De Rerum Natura*. And I do not intend this in the sense in which a writer of many works might, through the spite of time, be known to posterity only through one of them. With Lucretius obviously his book is his life. He is as much identified with it as Walt Whitman is with his *Leaves of Grass*. The sincerity we look for in Lucretius is not simply that of a sensitive artist who will not cheapen his theme. He has a personal statement to make. Of the *De Rerum Natura* we may surely say, Who touches this book touches a man.

The opinion I wish to maintain is that the polemic of Lucretius was not directed exclusively, or even mainly, against popular superstition, but that the object of his attack was the state cult as the mainstay and propagator of superstition, and that he had special reason in the circumstances of his own day for the acerbity of his attack.

I shall seek first to support these opinions by an examination of the opening lines of the first book of the *De Rerum Natura*. We should expect the poet to make his intention, and the scope of his work, clear at the outset. We shall find that in the first one hundred and fifty lines he has done so.

Readers have been filled with equal admiration and astonishment by the Invocation to Venus with which the poet has chosen to begin his work—admiration for the spirit and execution of the passage, astonishment that a poet supposed to have taught the indifference of the gods to mortal things should have falsified his own doctrine at the outset by beginning with a prayer. While the admiration remains, the astonishment has been much abated by a better understanding of the Epicurean view of religion as a whole, and by a closer examination of this passage itself. It was the teaching of Epicurus that belief in the divinity of the celestial bodies as recommended by philosophers was to be wholly rejected, but that the popular belief in the anthropomorphic gods of Greek tradition was to be accepted with reserve. It is quite natural, therefore, and in the right Epicurean tradition, that Lucretius should begin with an invocation to a goddess. And it is also worthy of every emphasis that the giving up of the first forty odd lines of the poem to one of the most earnest and beautiful prayers ever composed by human lips is an indication of the kind of religion that is *not* being attacked when the terrific onslaught on *religio* opens at line 62.

Before we consider the attack on *religio* there is a further point that needs to be considered. Epicurus had recommended belief in the popular gods, but with certain far-reaching corrections of the popular conception of their nature. This reformed theology Lucretius is careful elsewhere in his poem to expound. In Book II (600–643) he has occasion to repeat the mythological account given by the ancient poets of Greece of the worship of the Mother of the Gods. This he at once follows up with the Epicurean theory of the true nature of the divinity. The poetical account, he says, is beautifully told but untrue. "For the nature of the gods must ever in itself of necessity enjoy immortality together with supreme repose, far removed and withdrawn from our concerns; since exempt from every pain, exempt from all dangers, strong in its own resources, not wanting aught of us, it is neither gained by favours nor moved by anger." In our printed texts of the poem no such explanation is appended to the Invocation to Venus. But it has lately been shown (in my opinion beyond all reasonable doubt) that it was the intention of the poet to work a similar statement of the Epicurean doctrine of the divine nature into this opening passage of his poem.[2] This would have made it clear in what sense an Epicurean could sincerely pray, and what kind of help he could rightly look for from a god.

In order to get a correct understanding of the attack on *religio*, which then follows at once, it is vitally important to remember that the poem opens with a prayer, and was intended to continue with an exposition of the Epicurean view of true religion. First the positive religious teaching of the Master, then the praise of him for saving mankind from false religion.

Let us now consider again the famous lines in which the attack on religion is begun:

"When the life of man lay foul to see and grovelling upon the earth, crushed by the weight of religion, which showed her face from the realms of heaven, lowering upon mortals with dreadful mien, 'twas a man of Greece who dared first to raise his mortal eyes to meet her, and first to stand forth to meet her: him neither the stories of the gods nor thunderbolts checked, nor the sky with its revengeful roar, etc."

Here it is surely clear that the religion which lowered upon mortals with dreadful mien, and of which the most typical representative is Zeus with his thunderbolt, is that useful political variety we met in Theognis, Pindar, Critias, and Plato. And this identification may help us to understand, what is otherwise obscure, why Lucretius should claim priority for Epicurus in his daring venture. Of critics of popular religion there had been plenty before Epicurus; but, as we have seen, no one before him had organized a movement to emancipate men from the terrors of the organized State cults. Finally, the passage contains evidence of another sort upon the character of Epicurus and his movement. It is notable that while the traditional account in ancient and modern times makes Epicurus out to be a weakling whose instinct was to slip out of the world of affairs in order to avoid trouble, the first quality his Roman disciple chooses to celebrate in him was his daring, his *audacia*. I submit that courage is not the prime requisite in a man who sets out to attack what can properly be termed popular superstition. Those challenging lines in which Lucretius appraises the qualities exhibited by Epicurus in his task,

> "primum Graius homo mortalis tollere contra
> est oculos ausus primusque obsistere contra,
> quem neque fama deum nec fulmina nec minitanti
> murmure compressit caelum,"

were never sung in celebration of a man setting out to attack popular superstition in the sense of a pathological state of the individual soul prevalent among humble and ill-educated people. We are not reduced to conjecture here. We have from the pen of Plutarch, who was a staunch upholder of political religion, a lively and sincere attack on popular superstition which is well worth reading, and on the composition of which he deserves every compliment for his good sense, public spirit, and humanity. But nobody on the head of it would feel moved to such admiration as Lucretius felt for his Master; nobody would think of Plutarch as a sort of Prometheus defying Zeus for having written it. No, the courage was required by Epicurus because what he was attacking (and what his disciple Lucretius proposed to attack after him) was not the superstition of the little people but the organized religion of the great.

This will appear still more clearly in the sequel, in the example of the iniquity of *religio* which Lucretius chooses to give:

"This is what I fear herein, lest haply you should fancy that you are entering on unholy grounds of reason and treading the path of sin; whereas on the contrary often and often that very religion has given birth to sinful and unholy deeds. Thus in Aulis the chosen chieftains of the Danai, foremost of men, foully polluted with Iphianassa's blood the altar of the Trivian maid . . . that thus a happy and prosperous departure might be granted to the fleet. So great the evils to which religion could prompt!"

Here the villains of the piece are not the ignorant mob, they are the chosen chieftains of the Danai, foremost of men,

"ductores Danai delecti, prima virorum,"

picked out for loathing and scorn with all the emphasis of alliteration and a striking figure of speech. And what they are busy with is not a piece of popular superstition but an official act of state to secure a state purpose, the safe departure of their fleet on its mission of war. Here, too, we must note the deliberate intention with which Lucretius has contrasted the spirit of true religion and of false. His opening prayer to Venus was for peace; the murderous sacrifice of Iphigenia is for war. And that Lucretius has other wars than those of the Homeric age in mind he indicates clearly enough by the echo of the traditional Roman formula, *quod bonum felix faustum fortunatumque sit*, in the line

"exitus ut classi *felix faustusque* daretur."[3]

Though Lucretius, doubtless from motives of prudence, chose his example of the iniquities of religion from the remote past, he makes it plain immediately that it is the present he has in mind:

"You yourself some time or other overcome by the terror-speaking tales of the seers will seek to fall away from us. Ay indeed, for how many dreams may they now invent for you enough to upset the calculations of life and trouble all your fortunes with fear! And with good cause; for if men saw that there was a fixed limit to their woes, they would be able in some way to withstand the religious scruples and threatenings of the seers. As it is, there is no way, no means of resisting, since they must fear after death everlasting pains."

And not only is it the present he has in mind, but he envisages opponents whom he dignifies, and conceals, under the name of seers, who conduct a propaganda of terrifying tales, which are not errors but deliberate inventions, the most important of which is a doctrine of eternal torment after death; which belief is inculcated as the most effective way of crushing any possible spirit of independence. Against all this Lucretius proposes to set a true philosophy which will explain the nature of the universe, of the human soul, and of the gods. Such is the programme of the *De Rerum Natura*. Only incidentally is it a war on popular superstition; the real object of its attack is the state cult, that cult of which Mommsen said that the essential characteristic was "the conscious retention of the principles of the popular belief, which were recognized as irrational, for reasons of outward convenience."

Yet many modern critics, in spite of what the poet says, are convinced that there was nothing in the circumstances of the poet's day to justify the strength of his protest. Thus Regenbogen, after recalling the passage in Polybius in which he commends the Roman Senate's inculcation of superstition by means of the state cult, adds "this time was over when Lucretius wrote. His representation of religion and its power is, like many other things in him, an anachronism. The tragedy of his life and work results in no small degree from this fact." Lucretius becomes a sort of Don Quixote. His life is tragic, his work is tragic. He is noble surely, but not so noble as pathetic.

This is also Bailey's view, who states on the evidence of Cicero in the *Tusculans* that fears of the after-life were all but unknown in the Rome of Lucretius. He, too, is assured that Lucretius was fighting wind-mills. His view is that Lucretius took over from Epicurus the whole of his polemic against the fear of suffering in the after-life, and that the explanation of the violence of his denunciation of these eschatological myths is to be found in his lack of mental balance. "In his slightly abnormal state of mind it became an obsession."[4] Lucretius, therefore, so far from being the liberator of the minds of his fellows, was the solitary dupe in his society of the exploded superstitions of another epoch and another land. So much for the marvellous third book of the *De Rerum Natura*. The theory of the pathological nature of genius has never achieved a more striking result.

And what is the evidence for the slightly abnormal state of the poet's mind? It seems only an example of the fact that if you throw a lot of mud a little is bound to stick. A hostile notice of the poet's life, preserved to us from antiquity by St. Jerome, reports the tradition that he was mad. This evidence is recognized as bad. But insufficient evidence of madness can hardly be accepted as sufficient proof of abnormality. Meanwhile the function of the theory of abnormality is clear. There being no motive for the passionate earnestness of the poet discernible in the circumstances of his age, it is necessary to account for it in some other way.

The theory, though convenient, was superfluous. For the theory of the *anti-Lucrèce chez Lucrèce*, originated by Patin, has satisfactorily performed the same function for over a hundred years, and to judge by its adoption by Sinker in his *Introduction to Lucretius* (1937) is still a favourite. The French Catholic critic, to discount the eloquence and zeal with which the Roman poet supported a view of the nature and destiny of the human soul that was the opposite of his own, developed the theory that wherever Lucretius is most earnest in his argument, it is because he is arguing against his own inner conviction. Therefore if he brings twenty or thirty proofs of the mortality of the soul, this only goes to show that he was secretly convinced of its immortality. Now this theory of the *anti-Lucrèce chez Lucrèce* may be very important—for students of M. Patin. It is hardly of such importance in the history of Lucretian criticism as to have been allowed to occupy almost all the short space Sinker had to give to his analysis of the genius of the poet.[5] With Sinker the tendency to reduce the spiritual excitement that pervades the work of Lucretius to no more than evidence of internal disharmony reaches its final goal. His conclusion is: "The anxious and passionate missionary spirit that is evident throughout the *De Rerum Natura* is due not so much to a disinterested wish to instruct Memmius, nor even to a wish to convert mankind, as to Lucretius' desire to force *himself* to the mould of the master who was so different from him." In Book I, 932, Lucretius announces his purpose in writing in the following terms:

"religionum animum nodis exsolvere pergo."

("I am setting out to unloose the mind from the knots of religion.")

How little, it seems, he understood himself. He should

it was indeed the opinion of Macaulay that the Epicureans had "exaggerated immensely the effect which religious horrors and the fear of future punishment had on their contemporaries, for the purpose of exalting their master, as having delivered mankind from a horrible mental slavery." But this opinion of Macaulay's is of less interest in itself than for the comment it called forth from one who was a better scholar though a less eminent man than he. H. E. P. Platt[8] refers to the opinion of Macaulay, and avows his own contrary belief: "To myself, however, and I think to most readers, Lucretius appears, if ever man did, to write in grim earnest." He then comments upon the apparent contradiction, that certain Latin authors laugh at these fears, and suggests a solution: "I think modern experience supplies an explanation. Fifty years ago" (he was writing in 1905) "the prevalent teaching was that the majority would be doomed to eternal torments. That was the doctrine commonly heard from the pulpits, and set forth in books for children. Yet a student, two thousand years hence, of English literature of that period will find hardly any traces of such teaching. I infer, then, that literature is here an insufficient guide; and that, in spite of Cicero and Caesar, the doctrine of future torments was taught in the time of Lucretius, and revolted him, as the like doctrine has revolted some people in our own days."

Platt's explanation, though far from complete, is on the right lines. We shall advance the argument further if we take up his allusions to Caesar and to Cicero. The reference to the former is to the famous occasion, during the debate on the punishment of the Catilinarian conspirators, when Caesar, who was then Pontifex Maximus, denied openly in the Senate a future life in terms which would seem to imply that many of the Senators would agree with him.

The reference to Cicero is principally to a familiar passage in the *Tusculan Disputations* (i, 48), in which Cicero is himself criticizing the claims of the Epicureans. "I often wonder," he says, "at the extravagance of certain philosophers who marvel at natural science and in the transport of their joy render thanks to its discoverer and founder and do reverence to him as to a god. They say that through him they have been set free from tyrannous masters, from unending terror and daily and nightly fear. What terror? What fear? Where is the old woman so silly as to be afraid of the bugbears of which you gentlemen would, it appears, have been afraid, if you had not studied natural philosophy?" On this Sellar comments: "Cicero is a better witness than Lucretius of the actual state of opinion among his educated contemporaries. The exaggerated sense entertained by Lucretius of the influence of such terrors among the class for whom his poem was written, is a confirmation of his having acted on the maxim λάθε βιώσας (live out of the world)." And on this again Regenbogen comments: "The Roman nobility must have found the poet's holy zeal either comic or shocking."

When Sellar speaks of "the class for whom" Lucretius wrote, and when Regenbogen reflects what the effect of his poem must have been on the *nobility*, they inadvertently raise the point that serves to clear up the confusion in which the topic has so long been involved. What was the class for which Lucretius wrote? In the narrow sense, without doubt, the educated governing class. Memmius, to whom he addressed his poem, was a member of this class; the idiom is that of the governing class of Rome. But if we ask, whom was the poem meant to serve?, the answer is "the general mass of the people." Memmius is simply the individual to whom he addressed what was meant for mankind at large. Thus, in the prelude to his Fourth Book, in which he speaks to us more intimately than anywhere else about his intentions and the technical problems they raised for him as an artist and teacher, he tells us that the poetical graces are intended to make the physical doctrine more palatable and, in doing so, makes clear the wider audience he has in view: "So I now, since this doctrine seems generally somewhat bitter to those by whom it has not been handled, *and the multitude shrink back from it in dismay*, have resolved to set forth to you our doctrine in sweet-toned Pierian verse, etc." He clearly thinks that, if he can succeed in interesting Memmius, he may succeed in reaching a wider audience too.[9] To repeat what is essential to the understanding of the matter, the Epicureans had but one doctrine for all classes and Lucretius could not but think beyond the individual to society in general.

But this would not be true of Cicero and of Caesar. Caesar, when he spoke in the Senate, knew that he was addressing the organ of oligarchical government. A sceptical remark from him, even as Pontifex Maximus, is evidence of nothing but his realism and his contempt for the hypocrisy of his fellow senators. It affords no evidence at all of the state of feeling on the question of the after-life among the people generally.

Similarly Cicero's disavowal of belief in the myths about the next world, among a circle of philosophic friends, implies no more than Aristotle's casual comment to his audience in the Lyceum on the political function of myths. But it misses the point of the Epicurean campaign, probably deliberately. The Epicureans aimed at sweeping such superstitions out of the minds of the people, where we have every reason to suppose that they still existed, and where Cicero, as we shall see, was sometimes anxious to implant them.[10] They further had the ambition to sweep out of the minds of men like Cicero himself the Pythagorean and Platonic belief in the immortality of the soul which Cicero, in the same passage of the *Tusculans*, immediately goes on to avow. Neither the Caesarian nor the Ciceronian reference, therefore, afford the slightest evidence of the unreality of the terrors, and errors, which the Epicureans sought to dispel. The terrors existed in the populace at large; the errors in the mind even of the educated governing class. And, said the Epicureans, where error still lurked, there terror might easily raise its head.

Nothing, indeed, proves more clearly the alert awareness on the part of Lucretius of the actualities of his day than the passage in the opening of the Third Book[11] where he discusses the fear of death. It is written with the closest relevance to the picture which emerges from the pages of Cicero we have just been considering. Having first praised Epicurus for banishing from men's minds the fear of punishments in the life to come in Acheron, Lucretius goes on to discuss the very type represented by Cicero and his friends, namely those who for various philosophic reasons avow their disbelief in the terrors of the next world, but when in trouble, through lack of a sufficient understanding of "the nature of things," drop back into them. The passage is thoroughly Epicurean in tone. From Epicurus comes the idea that at the root of civic ambition lies the very fear of death of which the great ones of the world claim to be free. But though the passage is Epicurean in doctrine, it is completely thought out afresh in terms of Roman life.

It may be well to pause for a moment to consider additional evidence of the relevance of the tone and argument of the *De Rerum Natura* to the actual circumstances of its day. The evidence may be of two kinds, that which rises from the general atmosphere of the poem, and that which concerns particular passages. Of the former kind none, perhaps, is more convincing than the attitude of the poet to rival philosophers. In the Athens of Epicurus, although a special attention might be directed to the contemporary school of Stoicism, yet the opinions of the Academy and the Lyceum could not but be frequently present to the mind of the Master in his writings or his discussions. To Lucretius the situation presents itself in quite another light. There is only one rival school, that of the Stoics; and Lucretius does not so much dispute the opinions of schools older than theirs, as dispute the Stoic use of them. Philosophy has become a single tradition of which Epicureans and Stoics are the rival heirs. So much is this so that Lucretius often is not concerned to name his opponents, He says "they," and it is understood to whom he refers. But this corresponds to the situation of Rome in the middle of the first century B.C., not to that of Athens in the beginning of the third.

Similarly, if we now come to derive an argument from a particular passage, when in the opening of the Sixth Book Lucretius has expounded the atomic theory of thunder and lightning in accordance with the orthodox Epicurean view, he at once proceeds to make a Roman application of his doctrine. My explanation, he says, is the proper attitude to these phenomena; one ought not to thumb Etruscan rolls in the vain hope of learning from them how to discover in the thunder and the lightning the hidden purpose of the gods. But such thumbing of Etruscan rolls was still a living tradition in Rome; M. Tarquitius and A. Caecina were expounding in Latin the significance of lightning as a revelation of the divine mind; and Varro and Nigidius Figulus were giving their support. It was indeed a hoary superstition that Lucretius attacked when he attacked the

Etruscan lore of thunder and lightning; but, alas, it was a superstition that not only still survived but was having fresh life pumped into it by his educated contemporaries. Further proof of the actuality of the *De Rerum Natura* will meet us as we proceed.

Let us now resume the chronological thread of our enquiry from the year 173 B.C., when the Senate expelled the Epicurean philosophers from Rome. The evidence we possess is against the view that the Senate had much success with its policy of repression; for it is apparently in the middle of the same century that we must place the activity in Italy of Gaius Amafinius, the first man known to us to have popularized the ideas of Epicurus in the Latin language. Of the effect of his teaching Cicero speaks in the *Tusculans*. Deploring the tardy appearance of the various Socratic schools in Rome, he continues: "To fill the gap left by the silence of the various upholders of the Socratic tradition came the voice of the Epicurean Gaius Amafinius, and by the publication of his works the crowd had its interest stirred, and flocked to the teaching he advocated in preference to any other, whether because it was easy to grasp, or because of the seductive allurements of its doctrine of pleasure, or possibly because, in the absence of any better teaching, they clung to what there was. After Amafinius again there came a number of imitators of the same system and by their writings took all Italy by storm."[12]

This remarkable passage not only reveals to us the early and rapid popularity of Epicureanism in Italy, but suggests very strongly the mass character of its appeal. It was a ferment in society. In another passage Cicero not only reinforces our understanding of the strength of the movement but gives us a hint that it was, if only loosely, organized. "There is a class of men," he writes, with reference to the Epicureans, "who wish to be called philosophers and are said to be responsible for quite a number of books in Latin, which I do not for my part despise, for I have never read them; but as on their own testimony the writers claim to be indifferent to definition, arrangement, precision, and style I forbear to read what affords no pleasure. What followers of this school say and what they think is not unknown to anyone of even moderate learning. Inasmuch, therefore, as by their own showing they do not trouble how they express themselves, I do not see why they should be read except in the circle of those who hold the same views and read their books to one another."[13] In this phrase, the "circle of those who hold the same views and read their books to one another," we shall surely not be wrong in seeing evidence of the extension to Italy of the organized study groups we know to have been characteristic of Epicureanism.

As regards the content of the teaching in these Epicurean groups, in spite of the sneer of Cicero at "the seductive allurements of its doctrine of pleasure," the evidence is that these Latin writers devoted themselves almost exclusively to the exposition of the physical side of the system.[14] The significance of this is beyond dispute. A popular movement to teach Epicurean physics means a popular movement to abolish belief in the political function of the gods. And here it is of interest to note a contradiction to the usual picture painted of the religious scene in ancient Rome. That picture generally shows an enlightened Senate struggling to stem the tide of Oriental superstition that welled up from the motley populace below. But here was a powerful movement of rationalism spreading from below, carrying Italy by storm, as Cicero put it. And its reception from above was anything but encouraging. And yet Epicureanism was, in fact, the one doctrine that might have prevented the capitulation of Western Europe before the Oriental superstitions that finally submerged it.

"Cicero," Reid tells us, "hated and despised Epicureanism most sincerely, and one of his chief aims in undertaking his philosophical works was to stem the tide of its popularity in Italy."[15] But the hatred was not such as could be described merely in philosophical terms. When Cicero in the *Tusculans*, after expressing his profound admiration for Plato's argument (in *Phaedrus*, 245) that the soul is eternal because it is self-moving, proceeds: "All the *plebeian* philosophers—for that seems the proper name for those who disagree with Plato and Socrates and their school—may lay their heads together, and not only will they never unravel any problem so neatly, but they will not even appreciate the logic of the argument"—when Cicero expresses himself in this fashion with reference to his opponents, the Epicureans, we understand precisely the force of the word *plebeian*. And when in the course of the attack on the values of the oligarchy with which Lucretius opens Book Two, we come again on the same significant word:

> "nec calidae citius decedunt corpore febres,
> textilibus si in picturis ostroque rubenti
> iacteris, quam si in *plebeia* veste cubandum est,"
>
> ll. 34–36

("fevers do not sooner quit your body if you toss on embroidered purple sheets than if you lie in a *plebeian* blanket"),

we may ask ourselves whether we have not again one of those little evidences of the actuality of Lucretius's writing which are so easy to overlook, and one, moreover, full of significance. Lucretius knew very well what was the doctrine of the "aristocratic philosophers"; he could have no objection to the description of his own as plebeian.[16]

A mystery has always surrounded the attitude of Cicero to Lucretius. We know from his own words in a letter to his brother Quintus that within a few months of the death of the poet he had read the *De Rerum Natura* and acknowledged his admiration both of its art and its genius; and his familiarity with the poem is borne out by many passages in his writings. But he never elsewhere refers to the poet by name. It is hardly credible that this should be an accident. The *Tusculans* was written within ten years after the death of Lucretius; yet, in his opening chapters Cicero claims that "Latin literature has contributed nothing to philosophy"; and in the passage already quoted from the Second Book he refers to the many Latin books on Epicureanism and says that he has never read them. That this is false with regard to the *De Rerum Natura* we know. It would seem to be false with regard to other Epicurean writers also. Thus in his correspondence with Cassius, in the very year in which he wrote the *Tusculans*, he jokes about the technical terms to be found in the writings of the Latin Epicureans, which would seem to imply acquaintance with the books he says he has not read.[17] I have elsewhere stated my view of this inconsistency, namely, that Cicero has no reluctance to admit his acquaintance with Epicurean writings in his private correspondence, but is unwilling to do so in his formal works.[18]

Such a reluctance on the part of Cicero would imply the existence of great tension in the Rome of his day between the Epicureans and the ruling oligarchy. And the fierce hostility of Cicero to the Epicureans is only the other side of the fervour which seems to puzzle some critics in

the work of Lucretius. The nature of this tension will become
clearer as we continue our enquiry.

First a word or two is necessary as to the composition
of the community of Epicureans in Rome and Italy. Cicero
in the *Tusculans* gives us the picture of a mass movement
of lower-class people discussing among themselves the un-
distinguished writings of their plebeian school of thought.
But this nameless multitude seems to bear no relation to
the long list of distinguished individuals, many of them
Cicero's own personal friends, of whom we hear as members of the sect. It was surely not to Siro's famous garden-
school near Naples, the school to which Virgil went to study
Epicureanism, that Cicero referred in such contemptuous
terms. Nor was it to Velleius and Lucius Manlius Torquatus,
nor to Piso, father-in-law of Caesar, nor to Crassus, the
orator, nor to Titus Pomponius Atticus, and other more
or less enthusiastic followers of Epicurus among the ruling
class. We are forced to recognize two elements among the
adherents of the philosophy of Epicurus in Rome and Italy,
on the one hand a numerous band of "little people," on
the other members of the governing class, attracted by the
teaching as a personal creed, but unwilling to push incon-
venient tenets *à l'outrance*.

Among the latter Cicero had no difficulty in picking
harmless exponents of the Epicurean creed to set up the
ninepins for himself to knock down in the hastily contrived philosophical dialogues with which he fed his literary
vanity. Such was the role of the Senator Velleius, more
distinguished as such than as a philosopher, whom Cicero
puts forward as spokesman of the Epicurean point of view
in his disquisition on *The Nature of the Gods*.[19] But Lucretius,
whoever he was socially (Mommsen thought he came from
"the best circles of Roman society," Regenbogen doesn't

believe that he was even a Latin, let alone a Roman),
obviously could be assigned no part in this polite literary
game. If his poem, as Mommsen wrote, was produced by
"horror and antipathy towards the world in which and for
which he wrote," Cicero and his friends were certainly
included in that world as being of the very substance of
the thing from which he shrank.

The composition of the *De Rerum Natura* was the culmination of an effort of Epicurean propaganda in Italy which
had lasted more than one hundred years.[20] The propaganda
had been unwelcome to the Senate from the start. Nevertheless, it had made headway, such headway, indeed, that
the philosophic effort of Cicero was mainly directed to
stemming the tide of its popularity. He hoped, by routing
the Epicureans in the field of philosophy, to complete the
victory he had achieved in the political field by crushing
the Catilinarians.[21] But Cicero was not the first opponent
in the field. We have seen that for Lucretius the philosophic
opposition was the Porch. To understand the temper of
the Lucretian polemic against the religion of the state, we
need to understand also where the Stoics stood in this
matter. A glance at the Middle, or Roman, period of
Stoicism is vital to the elucidation of our theme.

Stoicism, like Epicureanism, began with some degree of
opposition to the aristocratic schools of Plato and Aristotle.
There has been some dispute among authorities in recent
times as to the extent to which Stoicism, in its first phase,
might be called a revolutionary ferment in society. Bidez,
in his fascinating study *La Cité du Monde et La Cité du Soleil*
(1932), brought much evidence in support of this view.
This evidence Tarn in his Raleigh Lecture, *Alexander the
Great and the Unity of Mankind* (1933), sets himself, not
without some degree of success, to destroy. But the fact

remains that, whatever were the practical intentions of Zeno and his early disciples, they were responsible for many sayings capable of a socially subversive interpretation. These sayings concerned not merely such matters as traditional forms of worship and education, but proclamations of the natural kinship of men and the natural community of wealth. The whole of mankind, they taught, formed one great fellowship, *societas*. But what were the rights of the individual members of this society? Was it the heart of the Stoic teaching that all *ought* to have an equal share, even at the cost of some upheaval, which is the point of view for which Bidez claims recognition in the first phase of the history of the school? Or was the heart of the doctrine, as was certainly true in its last phase and as Tarn thinks to be characteristic of it throughout, that social differences do not matter, that underneath external differences all men are brothers, and that what is needed is, not to alter society, but to penetrate beneath it to the underlying harmony and find one's peace in contemplation of the divine mind that guides it all? More briefly, was it a philosophy of revolt or of resignation? In spite of all that Tarn finds to say, the evidence to me remains conclusive that the movement went through a process of change, from a stage in which the revolutionary element was strong, to one in which its whole ethos was a mood of resignation. Between these two extremes, and effecting the transition between them, was the period of the Middle Stoa, the period in which Stoic teachers formed the mind of the governing class in Rome.

The broad features of this transition have been brilliantly sketched by Bidez. The conquest of the Orient by Alexander resulted in monarchies with cosmopolitan tendencies, in which petty distinctions of race, religion, and city were to some extent effaced by the one great contrast between monarch and subject. Man thus denationalized needed a new morality to replace that founded on the conception of the city-state. This need Zeno had met by a fusion of elements old and new. He completed the Cynic ideal of the independent individual man, which had arisen in opposition to the identification of man and citizen characteristic of the city-state, by the notion of a new and wider law, the Law of Nature.

The new concept of the Law of Nature did not, however, find a ready acceptance. The leagues of Aratus and Philopoemen, the characteristic form of oligarchic activity in the Greece of this period, were attempts to revive the old particularism of Greece (cf. p. 161). And this was the cause that prevailed. The socialistic experiment of the Spartan King Cleomenes was defeated; and the connection of the Stoic philosopher Sphaerus with his plans caused Stoicism to be suspect with the supporters of the form of society that found expression in the Greek city-state, now essentially a narrowly oligarchic ideal. Under these circumstances Stoicism lost its connexion with practical affairs. The Stoic ideal was no longer felt to be realizable on earth; and a chimerical belief in a City of the Sun took its place. Justice reigned in heaven if not on earth, whence one day, according to the millennial hopes common at this time, it might be expected to descend.

Stoicism was, thus, disappointed in its hopes of a new world in Greece and the East, and the West so far had been considered as barbarous and consequently despised. But when Polybius discovered in Rome the promise of an imperialist power the eyes of the Stoic school were turned from East to West. "Abandoning their preaching on the deserted steps of the Porch in Athens, the successors of Chrysippus went and established themselves at Rhodes, then the centre of a vast international commerce, and there they became the educators of the Roman aristocracy. With Panaetius, the master of the younger Scipio and of his friend Laelius, a renovated form of the system appears, that to which historians of philosophy have given the name of the Middle Stoa." Henceforth the connexions which had brought Stoicism into compromising relations with revolutionary movements quickly fell into oblivion.

Of the steps by which the Stoic teachers rid their doctrine of its undesirable implications we have much evidence in Cicero. I quote a passage from his *De Officiis* which shows the Stoa adapting its teaching to life in the commercial town of Rhodes:

"As I have said above, cases often arise in which expediency seems to come into collision with justice, so that it is necessary to enquire whether there is a plain incompatibility or whether the two can be reconciled. The following is a case in point: Suppose for example an honest man is importing from Alexandria to Rhodes a great cargo of corn, at a time when the Rhodians are in want and even starving, and the market price is high; suppose also that he knows that several merchants have sailed from Alexandria and that he has seen their ships in transit laden with corn making for Rhodes; ought he to tell this to the Rhodians or say nothing about it and get the highest price he can for his own? Remember we are supposing our man to be enlightened and honourable. What sort of argument and debate will he hold with himself, since he is not the sort who would conceal the facts from the Rhodians if he thought it wrong, but is in doubt whether it is wrong or not.

In cases of this sort Diogenes of Babylon, that great and

weighty Stoic, used to take one view, his disciple Antipater,
a man of the shrewdest understanding, another. For Antipater used to urge that everything should be told, so that
the purchaser should not be ignorant of any single thing
which the seller knew. Diogenes used to say that the seller,
in so far as the civil law decided, was bound to declare
any defects in his goods, but for the rest he was to act
without deliberate deceit, while trying, as seller, to get the
best possible price. 'I have imported the corn,' the merchant
is entitled to say, 'I have put it on the market, I am selling
what is my own no dearer than anybody else, perhaps even
cheaper, if I have a bigger supply; who is being injured?'
But on the opposite side the argument of Antipater makes
itself heard: 'Can I believe my ears? Is it possible that you,
who ought to think first of your fellow-men and be the
servant of human society, you who were born under the
Law of Nature and have adopted as your rule and guide
in life principles of Nature which teach you that *Your good
is the common good and the common good is yours*, is it possible
that you will conceal from men the abundance and plenty
that are within reach?' To this Diogenes might perhaps
answer: 'Holding one's tongue is not the same as concealing things. I cannot be accused of concealing things
from you, if I do not now inform you what is the nature
of the gods and what is the highest good, though it would
be much more important for you to know this than to
know that wheat was cheap. But I am under no obligation
to tell you everything it might be to your advantage to
hear.' 'There you are quite wrong,' Antipater will reply,
'it *is* necessary, unless you have forgotten that human
society is a bond established by Nature.' 'I remember that
well enough,' Diogenes will reply; 'but is the society of
such a sort that nobody is to have anything of his own?

For if that is so, there ought to be no talk of selling at all; everything ought to be given away.' "

We see here plainly enough how the Stoics were forced, if they took their own principles strictly, to condemn ordinary commercial practice and put themselves at odds with society on a fundamental point. If they were unwilling to put themselves into this position with regard to society as they found it, then they could only shelter, like Diogenes, behind the civil law. But when they thus decided that it was necessary to render to Caesar the things that were Caesar's, it is difficult to see what was left that they were to render to the Law of Nature. The Stoic Law of Nature, indeed, was doomed to come off second best in every encounter with the Roman civil law.

Plutarch, when discussing the role of the Stoic Sphaerus in the socialistic land reforms of the Spartan King Cleomenes, compares the Stoic doctrines to the poetry of Tyrtaeus which inflamed the souls of young men, and then hastens to add that this fiery doctrine could be very dangerous. This piece of evidence as to the revolutionary character of early Stoicism has, I think, not been allowed sufficient weight by Tarn.[22] But the same "reformation" as made Stoicism innocuous to sharp practice in trade made it also innocuous to monopoly in land. This point comes up prominently for discussion in Cicero's treatise De Officiis.

Thus in Book I, par. 21, we read: "There is not such a thing as private property by Nature; it results either from ancient occupation, when men in old days moved into empty ground, or from conquest, law, bargain, sale, or lot. This is the way nations acquire their territories, and the same is true of individuals. Therefore since what once was by Nature common property has now become private property, *let each man keep what he has got.* But if anybody wants more than he has, he will do violence to human society." And again in par. 51: "Community of property is to be observed in this sense, that what is assigned to individuals by the law or civil code is to be held in the manner established by law. *For the rest* we can obey the Greek proverb, 'friends have all things in common.' " By such summary procedure is the Law of Nature subjected to the civil law of Rome.

If I understand Tarn aright, he will not have it that the advice of the Stoic Sphaerus had any influence on the land reforms of King Cleomenes, nor that the advice of the Stoic Blossius guided the policy of Tiberius Gracchus in his attempt to arrest the progress of land monopoly in Italy. I believe Cicero thought differently. At least, after purging Stoicism of any theoretical advocacy of common property in land, he proceeds by a natural transition to make his position clear on the matter of the Gracchan reforms ("The slaying of Tiberius Gracchus by Scipio Nasica was an exploit by a private citizen as memorable as the destruction of Numantia by the general Africanus," *De Officiis*, I, par. 76) and on the land reforms of the Spartan kings (see Book II, par. 80, where the revolutionary Spartan King Agis is made the villain of the piece, and Aratus, the destroyer of the socialistic experiment of Cleomenes, is lauded to the skies). So much in illustration of the process by which Stoicism was disinfected of its revolutionary associations when it had passed into its middle phase, that of becoming the official philosophy of the governing class at Rome.

But the services of the casuists of the Middle Stoa to their Roman masters went beyond this. Their great achievement was the investing the whole threatened system of oligarchical government with the authority of the new universal religion based on the doctrine of the divinity of the stars. The dialectic of Plato had, in the absence of any progressive science to supply it with material on which to exercise itself, degenerated into a barren logic-chopping and negative scepticism; but his astral religion had come into its own. This learned superstition had been worked up by the Stoics, with the aid of Eastern elements, into a grandiose system before which the mind of literally every philosophic school, with the exception of the Epicurean, was paralysed. And this system was given a new application. Polybius had recognized in Rome the one government that truly understood the use of superstition. The Stoics went beyond this. They recognized in Rome the true Cosmopolis, the true City of the World. Rome itself as she then was, not any vision of a transformed society as dangerous men like Sphaerus or Blossius might suppose, was the fulfilment of the divine plan. Plato's abortive effort to transform his own peculiar brand of astral gods into the gods of the city was repeated on a grander scale, and with success.

It was not gods whose nature could be comprehended only by a difficult geometrical argument that were called upon to exercise their civic function in Rome. The Porch was too wise to inscribe over its portals the warning of the Academy, Let no one enter here who does not understand geometry. Its gods were accessible to those of a lesser mathematical culture, which was altogether convenient considering the backwardness of the Romans in these studies. They carried a prestige with them, derived from their remote Eastern origin, far beyond that with which the idiosyncrasies of Plato's lofty genius could invest those of his own devising. Their deity was not buttressed by so formidable an array of intellectual argument as those of Plato's *Laws*, but was all the easier to believe in for that. And they were readily accessible through a technique of divination, adapted to the requirements of the smallest or the largest purse, which brought them into personal contact with those who could not aspire to a comprehensive philosophical grasp of the whole system.

The power of the new conceptions derived from the East to supplant the tradition of Greek rationalism in the minds of cultured citizens of the Roman empire in the West may be understood from the appreciation of them by Diodorus of Sicily, the younger contemporary of Julius Caesar and of Cicero, and author of a Universal History. In his Second Book, in the twenty-ninth and following chapters, he gives us his impression of the new wisdom from the East. The Chaldeans, he tells us, belonged to the ancient Babylonians. Their priesthood resembled that of the Egyptians; the priests were dedicated to the service of the gods and spent their whole lives philosophizing, being specially renowned for their knowledge of the stars. Their priesthood was hereditary; son learned from father, and was exempt from other public services. The authority of father over son, and the fact that the studies were begun in childhood and continued throughout life, gave the students an extraordinary grip of the subject. Moreover, the traditions were immemorially old and inalterably fixed. The whole system offered a striking contrast with Greek education, where a student approached philosophy without preparation and too late in life, and after a temporary application to it was drawn away by the claims of everyday life. A few, who apply themselves to the study in order to make a profession of it, may persist; but they are always innovating with regard to the most important doctrines and never follow their predecessors. Hence the contrast between the fixity of the traditional dogma of the Chaldeans, and the uncertainty, fluidity, variety, and self-contradictoriness of the philosophy of the Greeks. As for the content of the doctrine—the Chaldeans teach the eternal nature of the Cosmos, which has no beginning and will have no end. It is an orderly whole under the control of divine providence. None of all the things in heaven happens at random or of itself, but all are accomplished in accordance with a definite and established decision of the gods. And the priests, having observed the stars for very long and come to know the powers and the motions of each, can foretell much of the future to man.

It had been the work of the early Stoics to harmonize this astrological teaching with the tradition of Greek philosophy. The man who, in the middle of the second century, further adapted it to the requirements of the enlightened oligarchy in Rome was Panaetius. He came of a wealthy family in the prosperous island state of Rhodes. His opportunities for education had not been restricted by lack of means. He had studied in Pergamum and Athens before, as a man of graceful but encyclopaedic erudition, he found his proper setting in the Scipionic Circle at Rome. A friend of Polybius, he shared with him his enthusiasm for the Roman State and his interest in its governmental problems. In the Scipionic Circle both the Latin language and Greek philosophy found a new birth, largely under the inspiration of Panaetius, who thus became, as Arnold in his *Roman Stoicism* rightly claims for him, one of the chief architects of Graeco-Roman civilization.

The works of Panaetius are lost, but we are in no doubt as to the character of his teaching. Cicero was not an avowed Stoic; he liked to make it appear that in his heart of hearts he was more at home among the intellectual refinements of Platonism. But he thought Stoicism more suited to the public for whom he wrote, and it was largely by the translation and adaptation of Stoic models that he created a prose vehicle for philosophy in Latin. The *De Officiis*, with which we were concerned a little while ago, was adapted from Panaetius. It was from Panaetius that Cicero learned how the seeming extravagances of Stoic thought might be brought into harmony with the civil law.

But the coping-stone of the Stoic achievement was the elaboration of a new civic religion by which the existing state of society was consecrated as being the pattern of what god in his wisdom had ordained for man. Polybius, who had been an active politician in a Greece torn asunder by class-war before he was brought to Rome, and who had been preoccupied with the problem of achieving a more stable society there, had felt that one of the disturbing elements in Greece was the emancipation of the mass of the people from superstition, and the carelessness with which Greek leaders of society regarded the decay of political religion. He was himself so sensible of the dangers of the spread of enlightenment that he was prepared in this one matter to compromise with his ideal of historical accuracy and to recommend that a proper proportion of pious fiction should be allowed the historian.

But in his exile and captivity he was amazed and delighted to find that the Romans, with their practical good sense, had solved the problem of the control of the masses by a thoroughgoing organization of superstition. To Polybius, and to his friend Panaetius, it appeared that the political wisdom of Rome was such that she must rightly become mistress of the world. They became Roman imperialists. But they were something more than that; they became the first conscious theoreticians of Roman world dominion. The spread of Roman power, however, did not mean to them a nationalistic enterprise in which Italians were to lord it over Greeks. In this they could hardly have joined with enthusiasm. It meant rather a reorganization of civil society throughout the inhabited world in the sense of a restoration of the oligarchy to power and the proper subordination of the lower elements in the population. To the achievement of this end Polybius recognized that Rome had made an essential contribution in her capacity to organize, among other things, the domain of political religion. What the Greek thinkers might hope to contribute was a more conscious understanding of the problem in its world dimensions and its philosophical implications. In a word, they could provide a political religion adapted not only to the needs of the City of Rome but to the universal Empire of Rome. This was the work of the theoreticians of the Roman period of Stoicism.[23]

The Stoics recognized three types of doctrine about the gods—the mythical, the political, and the natural. The mythical was that handed down by the poets, and was appropriate to their entertaining work. The political was that which had been found expedient in civil society. The third was that which had been elaborated by philosophers in the various schools. Of these three types the Stoics condemned none. The first they would leave to the poets. The second they would impose on the mass of the people. But to the third alone would they allow any validity. This was the teaching adopted by Varro in his great work *Antiquitates Rerum Humanarum et Divinarum*. This work was being composed by Varro simultaneously with the composition of the *De Rerum Natura* by Lucretius, and it would seem idle not to recognize in them the simultaneous culmination of two long rival traditions.

We have lost Varro's treatise, but we possess the attack upon it of St. Augustine, in which he quotes verbally the sentences to which he objects; we may therefore feel confident that we are correctly informed as to the tone and content of the work. In his treatise Varro records that the Pontifex Maximus, Scaevola, that is the official head of the state religion, had contended for the recognition of the three types of religious teaching distinguished by the Stoics: that sung by the poets, that thought out by the philosophers, and that devised by the leading men in the State. Varro does not disguise the fact that in his own opinion the religion of the philosophers is the only one with any claim to truth. The subject-matter of this philosophical or natural theology is such questions as: Who are the gods? Where are the gods? What is their nature? Did they come into existence or have they always existed? Are they made of fire, as Heraclitus believes, or of numbers, as Pythagoras teaches, or of atoms, as Epicurus says? But these sort of questions, he adds, can more easily bear discussion between the four walls of the schools than outside in the market-place.[24]

Varro recalls that Scaevola had given warning of the danger of permitting the debates of the philosophers to escape from the schools into the market-place. What sort of opinions, Scaevola had asked, is it injurious to bring before the multitude? And he had answered: This sort of opinion—that Hercules, Aesculapius, Castor, and Pollux were not gods. Scaevola had therefore expressly concluded, and Varro supports his opinion, that "It is expedient that states should be deceived in the matter of religion."

Varro was the greatest intellectual figure in the Rome of his day. His book was enthusiastically received. There is no room for doubt that it was in line with the thought of governing circles. His work was published about the time Lucretius died. Cicero was studying Varro and Lucretius simultaneously. In a private note to his brother he paid tribute to the genius of the dead poet, but his public eulogies were for Varro, and very flattering they were. Nor did he stop at eulogies. Being a statesman as well as a philosopher, he at once proceeded to the practical elaboration of the technique of state-control through religion. In 53 B.C. Cicero began the composition of his *Republic* and two years later he was busy on his *Laws*. In these treatises the Platonic technique of state-control through religion, on the improved Stoic model, is set out with great candour. Life, public and private, is to be involved in a network of religious observances. Priesthoods are to be kept in the hands of the aristocracy. The people, ignorant as to the procedure and rites suitable to these public and private observances, are to seek instruction from the priests. And the reason for this religious legislation is frankly given: "the people's constant need for the advice and authority of the aristocracy holds the state together."[25]

We know from another of his works that Cicero did not believe in divination.[26] But in the *Laws* he informs us that "the institution and authority of augurs is of vital importance to the state. I do not say this because I am myself one, but because it is vital to maintain this opinion. . . . What weightier privilege is there than to be able to interrupt a piece of public business if the augur says, *On another day*? What more wonderful thing than to be able to enforce the resignation of a consul? What more of the essence of religion (*quid religiosius*) than to be able to give or withhold the right of approaching the people or the plebs? than to be able to abolish a law which is not just?" It is Cicero himself, earlier in the same book, who underlines the significance of this last remark, by reminding his friend

Atticus, as they exchange compliments on the amenities of their vast estates, that men like Tiberius Gracchus would have had them broken up if it had not been for the ability of the augurs to "abolish a law which is not just."[27]

Such were the activities of the two leading literary figures in Rome in the years immediately preceding and following the death of Lucretius. Furthermore, their elaborate presentation of the case for saving society by the maintenance or inculcation of superstition is not an isolated phenomenon but is in line with the practice of Roman government as testified to by Polybius, and the theory of such government as elaborated by the Stoic teachers of the Roman governing class, after Polybius and Panaetius had opened up to Stoicism the new world of the West. It is under such circumstances that we are asked to look upon the attack of Lucretius on *religio* as the feverish self-tormenting of a sick mind fighting over again in times of peace the battles of the past.

Regenbogen has a passage[28] in which he puzzles himself over the different attitude of Epicurus and Lucretius to superstition. He points out that Epicurus, although opposed to superstition, was able to write books *On the Gods*, *On Piety*, *On Holiness*. But Lucretius makes no distinction between *religio* and *superstitio*, the norm and the excess; he unites them in the one condemnation. But if Regenbogen would open his eyes to the reality of the struggle in which Lucretius was engaged, he would see the reason for this. The distinction between religion and superstition was valid only in ruling-class circles where a few choicer spirits were anxious to preserve themselves from what Plato, in similar circumstances, had called the Lie in the Soul. If you are a supporter of the thesis that *It is expedient that States should be deceived in the matter of religion*, and are in fact actively engaged in the concoction of the best lie for the purpose, then the question of not becoming yourself involved in it assumes a new and practical aspect. The lie is called *superstitio*, the error in which the masses are to be involved. But for one's private happiness in this world and the next it is important oneself to hold a correct view of the divine nature, which correct view, to distinguish it from the error of the masses, we call *religio*. At the same time, although among ourselves we know that the state religion is *superstitio*, this is precisely the secret that must not be allowed to escape from the safe confinement of the schools to the market-place, where the knowledge would be dangerous to society. Accordingly, for the consumption of the masses, *superstitio* is to be labelled *religio*. And so Lucretius, who knew precisely what he was fighting, called it. That he did so is further proof of the relevance of his writing to the contemporary situation.

The organization of superstition, however, for reasons of state, though a contemporary problem, was not a new one. Lucretius must have known both its present and its past. Are we to presume that Lucretius did not know the opinions of Varro and Cicero? Is it conceivable that the famous passage in which Polybius describes the policy of the Senate in matters of religion was unknown to him? Had he never heard that Alcaeus and Philiscus, disciples of his Master, had been ejected from the City for "introducing pleasures"? Did he not know that Anaxagoras had been banished from Athens for a challenge to the obscurantism of that town? Was he ignorant that Plato had advocated death as the penalty for the beliefs he, as an Epicurean, was determined to propagate? Did he not understand his own position in the secular battle of humanity and enlightenment against the forces of privilege and persecution? There is no reason to doubt it.

Lucretius did not merely make his position clear as against contemporary supporters of the Noble Lie. He knew that he was but the last link in a long chain of those who had fought against the inculcation of superstition for reasons of state. Twice in his poem he makes a remarkable comparison between the tradition of Ionian science and the best organized priesthood in the history of the Graeco-Roman world. He calls the scientific tradition "more holy and much more sure than what the Pythian priestess gives forth from the tripod and the laurel of Phoebus." So far as I am aware, these passages have escaped adequate discussion, and to them I beg to invite attention.

There is a possible ambiguity in the interpretation of these words. It might be thought that Lucretius, looking about for a comparison that would stress in the most emphatic manner possible the reliability of the scientific tradition, had chosen the most holy and certain source of truth in the Greek world and, by a pardonable and readily intelligible exaggeration had claimed for science an even greater certainty than *that*. On this view his words would indirectly be a tribute to the oracle of Phoebus. But to mention this hypothesis is to dismiss it. True there are modern historians in abundance who so handle the question of the inspiration of the Pythian oracle that one is left in doubt, at the end of their recital, whether they do not in fact believe that the Source of all wisdom and power had for a season decided to impart His message to the world throughout the mouth of the Pythia at Delphi, when she had chewed enough laurel or inhaled enough sulphur vapour, and when her priests had been sufficiently "instructed," as the lawyers say. But nobody can suppose that

Lucretius shared their belief. To him the oracle at Delphi was an organized imposture, one of the evils of which religion was capable, and he meant by his comparison, not to compliment it, but to fling down his challenge to the whole tradition for which it stood.[29]

The first occasion on which he uses the comparison is in his First Book, and in just that place in the book which gives it the maximum of significance. He has been obliged by the logic of his theme to run through the history of Ionian science and establish the point that the atomic system is its proper culmination. In doing so he has been obliged to combat the opinions of men for whose mind and character he has the highest respect, men whose achievement excites in him the liveliest admiration and the humblest awe. In particular he has had to oppose some theories of Empedocles, for whom he felt a special veneration. In doing so he fears he may have given away a point to the opposition and accordingly chooses this moment to make his own position clear. These great men have, indeed, he says, greatly fallen in the fundamental principles of natural philosophy, but nevertheless "they gave out from the innermost shrine of their hearts answers that were far more holy and far more sure than what the Pythian priestess utters from the tripod and the laurel of Phoebus" (Book I, 737–739). The second occasion on which he uses the comparison (Book V, 111, 112) adds to its significance. It is now for his own words that he claims holiness and truth above that of the oracle of Phoebus, thus taking his place in the succession. Munro finds the comparison on this second occasion "somewhat pompous and inflated," and says that in the First Book it was "more in place." But that depends on how one understands it.

For the truth of the oracle of Phoebus was a crucial point

in the age-old battle we have been describing. It will be remembered that Pindar, who was so much at one with the oracle as to derive part of his income from it, had given his unreserved testimony to its omniscience and veracity. Belief in the oracle was thus inculcated in the finest achievements of the choral lyric in the form in which it was devoted to the service of the Dorian aristocracy. But in the form of the choral lyric which had been adapted to the service of Athenian democracy, the dramatic chorus, we find a different estimate of the reliability of Apollo. In the chorus of a lost drama Aeschylus makes Thetis complain of the falsity of the god of truth. At her nuptials, complains Thetis, Apollo was present and celebrated in song her fair progeny whose days were to be long, and who were to know no sickness. "And when he had spoken of my lot as in all things blessed of heaven he raised a note of triumph and cheered my soul. And I thought that the word of Phoebus, being divine and full of prophecy, would not fail. And now he himself who uttered the strain, he who was present at the banquet, he himself who said this— he it is who has slain my son." Euripides too, as is of course familiar knowledge, in several of his dramas developed the theme of the falseness of Apollo.

An attack by the Athenian democracy on the Delphic Apollo, the religious prop of Dorian oligarchy, is only what one would expect to find. Equally natural is it to observe that it was this attack on Apollo that provided Plato with one of his motives for the banishment of the poets from his Ideal State. It is he who has preserved for us the fragment of Aeschylus quoted above (*Republic*, ii, 383). He comments on it thus: "We will not praise these verses of Aeschylus. . . . These are the kind of sentiments about the gods which will arouse our anger; and he who utters them shall be refused a chorus; neither shall we allow teachers to make use of them in the instruction of the young, meaning, as we do, that our guardians, as far as men can be, should be true worshippers of the gods and like them."

Plato, as we have seen, felt proper to recommend the wisdom of Socrates by alleging the guarantee of the Oracle to its quality. And as he gave Apollo a role in philosophy, so also he gave him one in politics. "For the Delphian Apollo there will remain the most important, the noblest, and the chiefest acts of legislation . . . the erection of temples and the appointment of sacrifices and other ceremonies connected with gods and demi-gods and heroes. . . . For it is this god, I presume, expounding from his seat on the Omphalos at the earth's centre, who is the national expositor to all men on such matters."[30] It was for this god, in his character as fountain of political religion, that Lucretius reserved his special scorn. The exaltation of the Ionian tradition of natural philosophy over the authority of the Oracle of Delphi was no chance comparison, no idle hyperbole; it was an essential element in that revolution of the mind of society at which the poet, following in the footsteps of Epicurus, aimed.

---

[1] We can measure the progress of Epicurean studies between Mommsen and the present day by comparing the passage quoted from Mommsen in the text with the following from Sikes, *Lucretius, Poet and Philosopher*, 1936: "The poem is an epic whose hero is not so much Epicurus as Man: and the atoms from which Man is formed are not only significant as the prime elements of the Universe. Although senseless themselves, they contain, in their wonderful changes and interactions, the promise and the potency of all life—human as well as

animal and vegetable." This point he illustrates by quoting the fine lines, Book I, 250–256:

> "postremo pereunt imbres, ubi eos pater aether
> in gremium matris terrai praecipitavit;
> at nitidae surgunt fruges ramique virescunt
> arboribus, crescunt ipsae fetuque gravantur;
> hinc alitur porro nostrum genus atque ferarum,
> hinc laetas urbis pueris florere videmus
> frondiferasque novis avibus canere undique silvas. . . ."

("The rains perish when father sky has cast them into the lap of mother earth; but from them spring up the shining crops, and branches grow green upon the trees, and trees themselves grow and load themselves with fruit; likewise from the same source is bred our race and the race of beasts, from the same source we see glad cities bloom with children and the leafy woods resound on all sides with the young birds.")

For the Epicurean the history of man and civilization is part of the natural history of the universe.

2 See Regenbogen, *Lukrez: Seine Gestalt in seinem Gedicht*, 1932.

3 Cf. Cicero, *De Divinatione*, i, 45, 102.

4 *Phases in the Religion of Ancient Rome*. pp. 218–221.

5 Patin, *Études sur la Poésie Latine*, ed. 3, p. 128, quotes from the *De Natura Rerum*:

> "Molli quum somno dedita membra,
> effusumque iacet sine sensu corpus onustum,
> est aliud tamen in nobis, quod tempore in illo
> multimodis agitatur et omnes accipit in se
> laetitiae motus ac curas cordis inanes" (III, 113 ff.);

and comments:

> "Rien de mieux vu, de mieux senti, de mieux rendu. Qu'en conclut Lucrèce? que l'âme n'est pas, comme le veulent quelques philosophes, un être collectif, un resultat, une relation, une harmonie, qu'elle est une partie du corps. *Nous en tirons nous cette autre conclusion, qu'elle est distincte du corps.*"

This completely misses the essential point. Lucretius is concerned to prove that we have no evidence of soul apart from blood and nerves. Are blood and nerves abolished by sleep?

By such arguments Patin proved, to his own satisfaction, *la spiritualité involuntaire du Lucrèce*. But why must spirituality in Lucretius be involuntary, unless by spirituality one intends the belief that life exists apart from matter?

Patin is filled with admiration for the argument of Lucretius in support of freedom of the will, but thinks it inconsistent with the rest of his philosophy. But the inconsistency is wholly of his own making. It results from the fact that Patin cannot understand that for Lucretius free-will, so far as it exists, is not something that logically inheres in a definition of soul, but an historical product, an attribute of animals and men at a certain stage of their evolution. See Bk. II, 251–293; 973–990.

[6] *Op. cit.*, pp. 186–190.

[7] Franz Altheim, *A History of Roman Religion* (1938), p. 333.

[8] *Byways in the Classics*, p. 91.

[9] This passage is probably the clue to the reason why Lucretius chose a verse medium. The old Greek philosophers generally wrote in prose; but three of them, Xenophanes, Parmenides, Empedocles, preferred verse. This choice was probably dictated by the audience they wished to address. It is probable that both in the Greece of the fifth century and the Rome of the first, poetry would reach a wider audience than prose, that is as a vehicle for philosophy. I infer that Lucretius hoped to be widely read, and heard.

[10] In the *De Divinatione*, Cicero strikes a great blow at superstition. In the *De Legibus* he recommends it for political purposes. It is the typical dilemma of Classical Antiquity. The Epicureans alone stood unequivocally for enlightenment first, last, and all the time. The progress of Plato from the famous saying in the *Apology*, "An unexamined life is no life for a man," to the religious legislation of the *Laws*, is the saddest tragedy of intellect in the ancient world.

[11] Ll. 31–93.

[12] *Tusculans*, IV, iii, 6 and 7.

[13] *Tusculans*, II, ii, 5–7.

[14] Reid, *Academica* of Cicero, Intro., p. 21.

[15] *Op. cit.*, Intro., p. 22.

[16] Martha is of opinion that Cicero revealed his real opinion of Epicureanism when he protested impatiently, "Such language should rather be repressed by a censor than refuted by a philosopher." *De Finibus*, ii, 10. *Op. cit.*, p. 352.

[17] See *Ad Fam.*, xv, 16, i and 19, ii.

[18] See "The Gods of Epicurus and the Roman State," *The Modern Quarterly*, July 1938, p. 216. I note, to my satisfaction, that Martha is of the same opinion. My own view was formed independently.

[19] See Cicero, *De Natura Deorum*, i, 21, 57–58. On this passage Hadzsits (*Lucretius and his Influence*, 1935) remarks: "This statement tacitly places Velleius ahead of Lucretius; at the time of the composition of the *De Natura Deorum*, Velleius was a senator and the ranking Roman Epicurean."

[20] The relation of Lucretius to the Epicurean writers of prose in Latin who preceeded him is obscure. He claims in one place (v, 336, 337) to be the first to expound the Epicurean philosophy in Latin; but the passage suggests that he may have been thinking only of verse.

[21] So I interpret *Tusculans*, I, iii, taken in conjunction with II, ii, 5–7 and IV, iii, 6 and 7.

[22] Plutarch, *Cleomenes*, ii: ὁ δὲ Στωϊκὸς λόγος ἔχει τι πρὸς τὰς μεγάλας φύσεις καὶ ὀξείας ἐπισφαλὲς καὶ παράβολον, βαθεῖ δὲ καὶ πράῳ κεραννύμενος ἤθει μάλιστα εἰς τὸ οἰκεῖον ἀγαθὸν ἐπιδίδωσιν. (For lofty and passionate souls the Stoic doctrine can be dangerous and misleading, but when blended with a deep and gentle nature it brings out what is best in it.)

[23] I take the occasion to gather together here some sentences from Altheim's book which support my point of view as regards the influence of the Stoics:

"When the Stoa first set foot in Rome, mainly through the work of Panaetius and the decisive influence of the Scipionic circle, its theology came with it. Especially impressive was the division, going back probably to Panaetius himself, of religion into three parts—political, mythical, and natural. The idea that it was the statesmen who, as lawgivers in divine matters as in earthly, had placed in men's hearts the belief in divine power, . . . did not fail in its effect on the members of the senatorial aristocracy, who clustered round the circle of the younger Scipio." "Now came the age when the Stoa was to intervene decisively in the history of Roman religion as well." "The whole (i.e. of Varro's work on religion, with its Stoic inspiration) represented a comprehensive attempt to portray the whole of Roman religion from Stoic foundations." Roman religion "had taken refuge in the arms of the Stoic theology and of a science based upon it." "In so far as the collection of the tradition of religion was an occasion for realizing its extent, its meaning and its wealth, it became also a spur to raise to the rank of a norm of national life whatever had survived this new test and thereby proved its value." "The special importance of Cicero for the history of Roman religion consists in the fact that he is a true representative of the nobility, that he again gave emphatic expression to the inner connexion of state and state-religion." *Op. cit.*, pp. 334–338.

24 This characteristic, of keeping discussion of the truths of Natural Philosophy, of which theology is a branch, out of hearing of the people, is common to all the schools except the Epicurean.

25 See *Laws*, II, viii: *Quoque haec privatim et publice modo rituque fiant, discunto ignari a publicis sacerdotibus;* and xii: *continet enim rem publicam consilio et auctoritate optimatium semper populum indigere.*

26 *De Divinatione*, II, lxxii, 148. Contrast this passionate plea for the banishment of divination from the public and the private life of Rome with the solemn protestation in *Laws*, II, xiii: Atticus: *hac tu de re quaero quid sentias.* Marcus: *Egone? divinationem, quam Graeci* μαντικήν *appellant, esse sentio,* etc. With Cicero, as with Plato, the question must always be asked, Are these the words of the legislator or of the philosopher?

27 *Laws*, II, xii; and II, vi. Note also II, x: *quaeque augur iniusta nefasta, vitiosa dira defixerit, inrita infectaque sunto; quique non paruerit, capital esto.* Disobedience to the augurs is to be punished with death.

28 *Op. cit.*, p. 54.

29 For the behaviour of the Pythia, see Robert Flacelière, *Le fonctionnement de l'oracle de Delphes au temps de Plutarque* (*Études d'archéologie grecque: Annales de l'École des Hautes-Études de Gand*, t. ii, 1938).

The Pythia drew water from the spring Cassotis, which flowed by the navel-stone, mounted the high tripod, drank the holy water, chewed laurel leaves, breathed in the vapours of the *pneuma* and entered into a trance (pp. 104–105).

30 *Rep.*, 427 B.C.

CHAPTER FIFTEEN

AFTER LUCRETIUS

Sufficient evidence has now, I think, been adduced, to show that Lucretius in the *De Rerum Natura* was dealing with a contemporary situation. It is true that the state-religion of Rome was in decay. But the effort to revive its function as an instrument of oligarchic repression was a characteristic of the age. The great work of Varro on religion had raised again the whole question of the function of religion in the stabilizing of society, and emphasized afresh the claims of the Noble Lie. It must also be remembered that his work merely carried on the tradition of a hundred years of Roman Stoicism. Lucretius, on his side, stated, also in the most emphatic way, the rival view. Each philosophy represented a complete world-view. Each had its own view of the nature of things and of the course of human society. But the immediate practical outcome of Stoicism was the recommendation: *It is expedient that the people be deceived in the matter of religion.* The immediate practical outcome of Epicureanism was the intensification of the effort to enlighten the people in the matter of religion.

Whether this situation be regarded as justification for the intense earnestness of the polemic of Lucretius must still remain a matter of opinion. But I would claim that

sufficient evidence has been produced here to render inad-
missible the view that the explanation of the passion of
Lucretius must be sought wholly in any supposed psycho-
logical maladjustment. It was something in the Italy of his
own day that he was angry about, whether we sympathize
with his anger or not. It will not, I think, be found that
any writer has impressed subsequent generations with an
inescapable conviction of his greatness unless that writer
stood in some vital relation to the life of his time. Great
books are not distilled out of books; they are distilled out
of life. And the essential thing about Lucretius is that in an
age when the most learned author and the most eloquent
statesman were agreed that it is expedient that the people
be deceived in the matter of religion he summoned all the
resources of his learning and eloquence to maintain the
opposite view. He declared his intention of doing what one
man could to loosen men's minds from the knots of religion,
and called on his fellows not to stain their minds with the
loathly thing. Whether we agree with him or disagree with
him, the first step towards understanding him is to define
clearly what he was about. It is because, with all the advance
of modern scholarship, this essential point seems to be
obscured that I have felt impelled to write these chapters.

Furthermore, it is important to remember that, in so far
as the purpose of Lucretius has been understood in modern
times, it has not always been approved. The Lucretian
programme of popular enlightenment has not only ranged
against it some of the greatest names of the past. Not only
are Pindar, Plato, Aristotle, Polybius, Varro, and Cicero on
the other side. Judicious and candid modern enquirers take
the same stand. Such is the point of view that informs, for
instance, the whole of the earnest and influential work of
Warde Fowler on Roman religion and Roman society.

Nothing could be more eloquent of the dangers that are felt to infest this theme than Fowler's considered judgment:

"Looking at the matter historically, and not theologically, we ought to sympathize with the attitude of Cicero and Scaevola towards the religion of the State. It was based on a statesmanlike instinct; and had it been possible for that instinct to express itself practically in a positive policy like that of Augustus, instead of showing itself in philosophical treatises like the *De Legibus* . . . it is quite possible that much mischief might have been averted. But in that generation no one had the shrewdness or experience of Augustus, and no one but Julius had the necessary free hand; and we may be almost sure that Julius, Pontifex Maximus though he was, was entirely unfitted by nature and experience to undertake a work that called for such delicate handling, such insight into the working of the ignorant Italian mind."[1]

Every word of this passage is worthy of the closest attention; but it would be the subject of a different treatise to bring out all its implications and say why I regard them as unjustified. For the present I am concerned to urge this one point: If the weight of opinion ancient and modern is agreed that it was the duty of the State to use all the shrewdness, all the experience, all the delicate handling, all the insight into the workings of the ignorant mind which it could command, not to enlighten that mind, but to invent such fictions and embody them in such external acts of religion as would remove any "danger" that might result from the workings of the popular mind, then the possibility of such a society welcoming science or basing its life in any fundamental way on science was precluded. Science in such a society was doomed. And it was doomed by something extrinsic to its own nature. It was doomed by the political structure of ancient society.[2]

Martha has expressed in his own clear way his sense of the incompatibility between the carefully fostered superstition of ancient societies and a true science of nature. "At Rome above all, every man who ventured on a scientific explanation of a natural phenomenon seemed to be encroaching on the limitless power of the gods. In order to engage in science a man had to have the courage to declare his impiety. That is why the Romans remained so long in ignorance."[3]

For the false doctrines of the state cults—medicinal lies, as they appeared to his statesmanlike predecessors and contemporaries—Lucretius, with that gift for metaphor in which his genius is so frequently revealed, coined the phrase, "wounds of life" (*vulnera vitae*).[4] In the Augustan age this medicine was administered, or these wounds inflicted, with a lavish hand. Not to speak of the Augustan revival of the state cults, the loftiest literature of the Augustan age is essentially incompatible with a scientific outlook on life. Virgil is a great antiquarian, but is innocent of history. In his *Aeneid* the history of Rome, reconstructed on the Stoic model, becomes merely an illustration of the divine providence, a miraculous tale of a destiny foretold by oracles and guided by portents, with pedigrees going back to the gods for the chief actors. It joins hands with Pindar on one side and Prudentius on the other. Its extraordinary merits should not blind us to the deliberate elimination of a true science of nature and a rational view of history. If the account of human history in the *Aeneid* be contrasted with the account given by Lucretius in his fifth book, and if it be remembered that the *Aeneid* was taught in all the schools of the Empire while the teaching of the *De Rerum*

Natura was condemned, the total loss of the scientific conscience in the subsequent centuries becomes more intelligible.

Polybius had allowed to the historian the right to qualify
his professional veracity with a "statesmanlike" admixture
of the miraculous for the sake of the popular mind. Livy
takes full advantage of the permission. Edification rather
than truth is the guiding light of his spirit, and in his preface
he makes clear that history in his conception is not so much
a science as a form of national glorification. "We grant
the indulgence to the remote past of intermingling the divine
with the human with a view to exalting the beginnings
of cities; and if any people may claim the privilege of con-
secrating their origins by referring their foundation to the
gods, such is the military glory of the Roman people that
when they boast Mars in particular as their own, or their
founder's, parent, the human race at large may bear this
with the same submission as it bears their sway."[5] A Thucydides would have been as unwelcome in the Rome of
Augustus as an Anaxagoras.

In this matter we are not left to conjecture. Livy's Greek
contemporary, Dionysius, whose active career as a writer
was spent in Rome, takes Thucydides to task for his love
of truth and neglect of the prime duty of a historian, to
gloze unwelcome facts. His language is most instructive.
"A second function of historical investigation is to determine where to begin and how far to proceed. In this respect,
again, Herodotus displays far better judgment than Thucydides. He begins with the cause of the original injuries done
to the Greeks by the barbarians, and goes on his way till
he ends with the punishment and retribution that befell
them. Thucydides, on the contrary, starts with the incipient
decline of the Greek world. This should not have been
done by a Greek and an Athenian, etc."[6] In the Augustan

age the intellectual standards of the great past of Greece are dishonoured, though the craft of the writer never attained to greater perfection. Lucretius had maintained these standards with passion. He speaks of the upholders of the scientific tradition as "the grave Greeks who seek truth."[7] But the Roman conception of *gravitas* was innocent of any relation to truth. It is, on occasion, specifically the quality that could impose on the people belief in the politically necessary fiction. Livy, when he describes the imposing falsehood by which Proculus Julius persuaded the distressed and rebellious people of the immortality of Romulus, gives this characterization of its author: *gravis quamvis magnae rei auctor* (a man of such weight—*gravitas*—as to win acceptance for any statement).[8]

And this is precisely the type of character to which so ethical an author as the late Warde Fowler feels compelled to award the highest praise. He tells us that he can find in the whole mass of Cicero's correspondence hardly anything to show that Cicero had any sense of dependence on, or responsibility to, a Supreme Being. He tells us that, as far as the forms of religion were concerned, Cicero's interest in religious practice was confined to ceremonies which had some political importance. He tells us that Lucretius was a great religious poet, a prophet in deadly earnest, calling men to renounce their errors both of thought and conduct. And then he concludes by telling us that, looking at the matter *historically*, we ought to sympathize with the Cicero of the *Laws* and condemn the author of the *De Rerum Natura*.[9] What, then, is this view of history which can justify so strange a conclusion? We shall try to analyse it.

While the ancient writers themselves reveal openly enough that the object of the state cult was to keep the people quiet under the system of property relations that obtained, Fowler will have none of it. Polybius tells us that the object of the cults was to *frighten* the people. Cicero points out how essential the institution of augurs had been in preventing such movements as that of Tiberius Gracchus to break up the large estates. Fowler ignores these things. According to him the one object of the cults was to *comfort* the masses. "The governing classes were trying to quiet the minds of the people by convincing them that no effort was being spared to set right their relations with the unseen powers; they had invoked in vain their own local and native deities, and had been compelled to seek help elsewhere; they had found their own narrow system of religion quite inadequate to express their religious experience of the last twenty years."

These words are written with special reference to the religious legislation enacted during the Hannibalic invasion (that is, with reference, among other things, to the establishment in Rome of the worship of the Great Mother, in particular regard to whose cult Lucretius had begged his readers not to "stain their minds with foul religion"), but they fairly represent the mind of Fowler on the whole history of Roman religion. For him it is possible to bring the whole thing under the title of *The Religious Experience of the Roman People*[10]—as if the rich who buried their dead in mausoleums along the public highways and the poor whose dead were thrown into the common pit had one and the same religious experience; as if the Senate, who decided to establish a cult like that of the Great Mother and fetched in a blackened meteorite from Asia Minor for the purpose, which meteorite had obviously not been consciously missed by the great majority of the Roman people, but who also decided to root out by fire and sword a cult like that of Bacchus which the people had chosen to introduce for themselves—as if the Senate could be said in any sense to be united with the people in a common religious experience; as if the deceivers and the deceived ("it is expedient that the people be decieved in the matter of religion") can be said to have shared a common religious experience. *The Religious Experience of the Roman People* is a title under which an adequate history of Roman religion cannot be written.

In a recent study of ancient society I find the following paragraph: "Plato says that laws restricting the sale of property were not viewed with favour in oligarchies. This was because oligarchs were, he says, sharp-set for land as a main source of wealth, and such restrictions hampered the rate or even the possibility of acquisition of landed property. This is a statement of first-class importance, from the light it throws on the part played by the nobility in directing the economic policy and history of their respective states. That history, in Attika, is by no means to be conceived as a sort of humanly uncontrollable natural evolution, but as the outcome of a very deliberate policy of exploitation for which the oligarchical nobility must bear the responsibility."[11]

These are relevant words, for the tendency to represent events which have very definitely been controlled by human policy as being "a sort of humanly uncontrollable natural evolution" is by no means confined to the economic sphere. Religion is one of its playgrounds. In so acute and worldly-wise an historian as Nilsson, to choose not the worst offender, we read again and again such sentences as "Apollo saw," "Apollo decided," "Apollo this" and "Apollo that," until we begin to ask ourselves: Does Professor Nilsson really, perhaps, believe in Apollo? And, if not, why does he not rather say "The Delphic priesthood saw, decided, or what not?" In the latest historian of Roman religion, Professor

Altheim, this habit of assuming the objective truth of ancient religious beliefs has reached such a pitch that critics have suspected that he is not speaking figuratively, but literally accepts the existence of the pagan deities of Greece and Rome. But I would urge that thus to expunge human inventiveness from the development of religion, and in particular from such an aspect of religion as we have been considering, namely, the officially established state cults, is to falsify religious history in the way in which the writer whom we quoted above claimed that economic history had been deformed.

But we may even go further, and discover a still closer relevance in his words. For the oligarchical nobility who, according to our writer, controlled the development of economic policy and guided it into channels which facilitated the monopoly of land were the same persons who, in their capacity as senators and magistrates and priests, presided over the religious policy of their respective states and guided the religious life of the people into such forms as would best support the monopoly. The essential was to foster the belief that the oligarchical nobility were where they were by the will of heaven, and that any effort to dislodge them would be rewarded by condign punishment in this world and the next.

Such a programme, of course, never exists in its naked simplicity as the conscious mental attitude of a whole class in society. It reveals itself only in moments of unguarded candour, or when there is a crisis of thought; and then, as a rule, only as part of a complex of ideas whereby the noblest instincts may be enlisted on the side of obscurantism in thought and monopoly in wealth. Such was the case of Pindar and Plato. Such was the case of Cicero and Virgil. And such was the conception of society inculcated during the principate of Augustus by the Stoic poet Manilius, who wrote consciously to combat the view-point on nature and society of the *De Rerum Natura*. According to him the universe is constructed on the pattern of the aristocratic State. In the heavens themselves we can detect among the stars the degrees of rank and privilege of earthly society, the senators, the knights, the citizens, and the nameless mob. "But if to the people, who are the most numerous, strength had been given in proportion to their numbers, the whole universe would go up in flames."[12]

The Christians of the early centuries did not take the same view of the religious legislation of pagan society as has been taken by modern Christians like Warde Fowler. St. Augustine, in his *City of God*, discusses the question of the manipulation of religion by the governing classes in pagan antiquity and assigns a motive for it. I translate the passage:

> "*Book iv, Chapter xxxii.*
>
> *Upon what show of utility the governing classes among the pagans wished false religions to persist among the peoples subject to them.*

Varro tells us that as regards the generation of the gods the people were more inclined to the poets than to the philosophers, and that that was the reason why their ancestors, that is to say the old Romans, believed in the sex and generation of gods and supposed them to marry. But the reason, of course, was that it was the business of statesmen and philosophers to deceive the people in the matter of religion, and in so doing not only to set up the worship of devils but to take them as their example, for the chief delight of devils is deceiving. Devils cannot take possession

of men until they have deceived them; so the leaders of
the state, who were assuredly not just men but rather
devilish, persuaded the people in the name of religion to
accept as true what they knew to be lies, thus binding
them the more tightly to their form of society so that they
might subdue and possess them, as the devils also did. And
what chance had poor ignorant men of escaping the combined deceit both of the devils and of the leading men
of the state ?"

In this one point the Epicureans and the Christians, poles
apart as they were in other respects, joined hands. In the
narrative of Lucian we find the oracle-monger Alexander
warning away from the scene of the mystic pantomimes
by which he fleeced the people, "any atheist or Christian
or Epicurean." The collocation is interesting; it includes
all those who made evident their hostility to the religion
of the State. And just as the Epicureans were united with
the Christians on this point, so on the same point they
were separated from all the other philosophical schools.
Lucian assures us that the imposter Alexander enjoyed the
support of the Platonists, Stoics, and Pythagoreans. Elsewhere also he emphasizes the isolation of the Epicureans
in their protest against the superstitions of the time.[13]

But if the Epicureans and the Christians were united in
their opposition to the state cults, they differed in the means
by which they sought to free the people. Among the many
valuable elements which the Christian crusade united under
its banner for the regeneration of ancient society, physical
science was conspicuous by its absence. We have seen, in
the passage just quoted from St. Augustine, that he does
not reject belief in the gods of the heathen; he merely
regards them as malevolent powers, and renames them

devils, or demons. The New Testament, as Huxley stressed in a notorious controversy in the nineteenth century, is permeated with demonology; and in the second century of our era, Origen, the most learned of the Greek fathers of the Church, strongly supported this view. He did what one man could to undo the work of enlightenment that had been attempted by the Hippocratic author of *The Sacred Disease*. He imposed the idea that epilepsy and somnambulism were maladies of demoniacal origin, and might be considered as forms of possession. And with the cruelty that springs from fear and ignorance he laid extra burdens upon the sick. Epileptics were excluded from making presents at the altar. They were also excluded from communion, in the sense of participation in the eucharist. It was feared that their ailment was contagious. Unhappily, the future, at least for over a thousand years, lay with Origen rather than Hippocrates.[14]

Nor could even a knowledge of Hippocrates avail to stem the tide of superstition. The most learned of the Latin fathers in the second century, Tertullian, among the rich resources of his mind knew also Hippocrates. In his treatise *On the Soul* he considers that he disposes of three sources of information: philosophy, medicine, and Holy Scripture. He is well read in the philosophers, but handles them with enviable freedom, treating some of the greatest of them to the greatest disrespect. His opinion of the doctors of medicine, when he comes to discuss them, is of an altogether higher sort, and he is ready to bow to the entire authority they hold in their own domain. But his enquiry into them is subordinate to his endeavour to understand the truths of Christianity, and in case of conflict between science and Holy Writ he does not hesitate: the Scripture is surely right.[15] By such steps did science degenerate to the level at which we found it in our opening chapters in Cosmas Indicopleustes and in Prudentius.

But for this degeneration Christianity does not bear the blame. The uncritical acceptance of the Hebrew Bible as an oracle was not the cause of the decline of science, but merely a symptom. The tradition of a science of nature had long been trailing its slow length along, scotched like a poisonous snake by the adversary who really feared it, the privileged classes in society. In order to control society, it was necessary for them to control "truth." If anybody was to be free to lie, as Plato put it, it must be the government. But the privileged classes can never wholly control science, which draws its evidences from the five senses possessed by all men, and is the necessary enemy of blind authority in that its only appeal is its reasonableness, its only triumph its free acceptance by an instructed mind. Oligarchies, then, must discover other sources of "truth," the oracles of Delphi, Sybilline books, the voices of birds, interpreted by aristocratic priests, who alone have access to the mind of the gods. Above all, there must be maintained such a distance between the classes that when some great and good man rises up to tell the socially-necessary lie, his *gravitas* may be such as can carry the weight of what he says. For the entertainment of the privileged behind closed doors shall be kept alive a science of a kind. But he that publishes such science in the market-place is a traitor to his class. Such was the tone and temper of ancient society, and it was this tone and temper that was incompatible with the scientific spirit.

In sixth-century Ionia man faced Nature in the confident hope that by his unaided powers he would be able to wrest from her her secrets; and in his bold enterprise he came to feel himself engaged upon an ethical as well as a scientific task. Conscience acquired a new scope as man realized that his progress in knowledge meant submitting his mind to the acceptance of external fact, of external law; and that the understanding of this law gave him power to help or harm his fellows. *Philanthropia*, love of his fellows, became his inspiration as much as *theoria*, disinterested curiosity.

But the obstacles to the growth of this new knowledge and to the exercise of this new power proved greater, and other, than had been anticipated. Not only did Nature prove more complex than man had supposed, but political obstacles also intervened. If democracy dimly and fitfully perceived that its fate was linked with science, oligarchy had no manner of doubt that ignorance was its shield. The politico-religious organization of oligarchical society became increasingly opposed to the progress of science. Platonism, in one aspect one of the most strenuous efforts ever made by the mind of man to extend the domain of reason, is in another aspect an elaborate plan for the substitution of truth in the mind of the citizen body by an intricate system of lies.

Aristotle saved his scientific soul by a breach with Platonism where Platonism had lost touch with Nature, but he retained from Platonism the view that truth is the preserve of the élite, and that social order must be based on acknowledged superstition. That this oligarchic corruption of the roots of the popular intelligence was to some extent frustrated in Greek society was due to the Epicurean movement. Epicureanism was a phenomenon called into being by the circumstances of its time and place. It was in Athens that the conflict between Ionian science and the technique of controlling society through the Noble Lie first became clear. It was in Athens that the Noble Lie attained its most elaborate philosophical justification. It

was in Athens that a man was found who attempted to
attack the Lie at every point and undermine it, and to show
how life must be based on a rational knowledge of the
Nature of Things.

In the West the rulers of Rome achieved a degree of
success in the control of society through superstition that
was denied to the Greek oligarchies. Under the aegis of
Rome the progress of public ignorance was assured. Their
practice, commended by Polybius, and brought up to date
by the philosophers of the middle Stoa, received its final
consecration in the politico-religious writings of Varro and
Cicero. The same programme of the Roman oligarchy,
that found admiring supporters in Varro and Cicero,
called forth the passionate protest of Lucretius. The *De
Rerum Natura* is the last great cry of Greek science, expressing not only its devotion to truth but its devotion to
humanity. The poem is a protest against the dissemination of superstition by authority and an attempt to
resist it.

The widespread movement of popular enlightenment
out of which it sprang suffered a fatal blow with the overthrow of the Republic. One of the departments of state
in which the Principate most successfully and thoroughly
restored order was *religio*. A popular movement of enlightenment was no longer possible. A free mind like that of
Seneca could only groan inwardly under the obscenity and
inanity of the public cults. "These observances a philosopher
will maintain because they are imposed by law, not because
they please the gods." "The whole base throng of gods
assembled by a superstition coeval with time we must
worship, without forgetting that we do so to set an example,
not because they exist."[16] Where Lucretius attacks the
institution, Seneca contents himself with expressing his

personal disgust at it, while giving his approval to its fraudulent purpose.

The very understanding that there was such a thing as science, except for a few languishing techniques such as medicine or architecture, almost died out under the Empire. And as the next great challenge to the values of the oligarchy surged up, the challenge of Christianity, it was innocent of all knowledge of natural philosophy or of the true course of human history. It marched to battle under the inspiration of a new oracle, the Hebrew Scriptures, with no understanding of the element of human error and the element of human imposture they contain. Its own new scriptures, with their fresh share of errors and impostures, were soon accorded a like reverence. The sense of the necessity of a true knowledge of nature and of history for man's guidance of his destiny had been wholly lost. It was to be a millennium and more before men were again to realize that the human head, which produced them, is worth more than all the bibles and all the creeds.

---

[1] *Social Life at Rome* (1908), p. 326. Warde Fowler treats the religious legislation of the Romans as justifiable deception of the people. His disciple Cyril Bailey spreads over it the cloak of a still greater charity. "It is notorious that polytheism is always prepared to add new gods to its pantheon; Rome was in this respect no exception, and, *as she developed intellectually*, she was correspondingly ready to include new ideas in her theology" (*Religion in Virgil*, Oxford, 1935). This is surely too complimentary.

[2] The achievement of ancient civilization was the separation of science and the citizen. Hence the historical significance of the title of Professor Hogben's latest book: *Science for the Citizen.*

[3] Martha, *op. cit.*, p. 360.

[4] See Bk. V, 1197; and Bk. III, 63.

A suggestive beginning of an analysis of the metaphors of Lucretius was made by H. S. Davies in *Notes on Lucretius* (*The Criterion*, October 1931). The subject needs to be worked out.

[5] Livy, *Preface*.

[6] Dionysius of Halicarnassus, *Letter to Pompeius*, 769, 770. Translation by W. Rhys Roberts.

[7] *De Rerum Natura*, i, 640.

[8] Livy, i, 16, 5.

[9] The account of Fowler's opinions here given is drawn from the chapter on Religion in his *Social Life at Rome in the Age of Cicero*.

[10] This is the title of Fowler's study of Roman religion, published in 1911, three years later than his *Social Life at Rome*. It is interesting to see the title of the later book foreshadowed in the former.

[11] *Solon the Liberator*, W. J. Woodhouse, Oxford University Press, 1938, p. 147.

[12] *Astronomicon* v, 734–end.

[13] See the two essays of Lucian, *Alexander the Oracle-monger*, and *Philopseudes or the Lover of Falsehood*.

[14] Franz Joseph Doelger, *Antike und Christentum*, fascicule ii (Heft 4). Notice in Supplément critique Budé, 1934.

[15] J. H. Waszink, *Tertullien, De Anima*. Notice in Supplément critique Budé, 1934. In the *De Anima* will be found the source of Prudentius' views on the soul and the future life.

[16] See St. Augustine, *De Civitate Dei*, vi, 10.

Bibliography

ALTHEIM, F., *A History of Roman Religion* (Eng. tr.), 1938.

ARMSTRONG, A. H., *The Gods in Plato, Plotinus, Epicurus* (*Classical Quarterly*, July–October 1938).

ARNOLD, *Roman Stoicism*.

BAILEY, CYRIL, *Translation of the De Rerum Natura*, 1910.
Text of the De Rerum Natura (2nd ed.), 1921.
Epicurus, 1926.
Greek Atomists and Epicurus, 1928.
Phases in the Religion of Ancient Rome, 1932.
Religion in Virgil, 1935.

BENN, A. W., *The Greek Philosophers* (2nd ed.), 1914.

BEVAN, E. R., *The House of Seleucus*.

BIDEZ, J., *La Cité du Monde et la Cité du Soleil*, 1932.

BIGNONE, E., *L'Aristotele Perduto*, Firenze, 1936.

BOELSCHE, W., *Haeckel, His Life and Work*, Fisher Unwin, 1906.

BRUNOT ET MIELI, *Histoire des Sciences: Antiquité*, Paris, 1935.

BURNET, J., *Early Greek Philosophy* (2nd ed.).

BURY, J., *Nemean Odes of Pindar*, 1890.

COLLET, *History of Taxes on Knowledge*, Watts (Thinker's Lib.).

CORNFORD, F. M., *Before and After Socrates*, 1932.

CROISET, A., *Les Démocraties antiques*.

CUMONT, F., *Religions orientales dans le Paganisme romain*.

BIBLIOGRAPHY

DAVIES, H. S., *Notes on Lucretius* (*Criterion*, Oct. 1931).

DEMPSEY, T., *The Delphic Oracle, Its Early History, Influence and Fall.*

DOELGER, F. J., *Antike und Christentum.*

ENRIQUES ET SANTILLANA, *Histoire de la Pensée Scientifique I, Les Ioniens*, Paris, 1936.

FARRINGTON, B., *The Gods of Epicurus and the Roman State* (*The Modern Quarterly*, vol. i, No. 3).

FLACELIÈRE, R., *Le fonctionnement de l'oracle de Delphes au temps de Plutarque*, Gand, 1938.

FOWLER, W., *Social Life at Rome*, 1908.
The Religious Experience of the Roman People, 1911.

FREEMAN, K., *Epicurus—A Social Experiment* (*Greece and Rome*, vol. vii, No. 21).
An unusually sympathetic study.

GASSENDI, *De Vita et Moribus Epicuri.*

GILDERSLEEVE, B., *Pindar, Olympian and Pythian Odes.*

GOMPERZ, T., *Greek Thinkers.*

HADZSITS, *Lucretius and His Influence*, 1935.

HICKS, R. D. *Diogenes Laertius* (Loeb Library).

HIRST, M. E., *A Reference to Lucretius in Cicero Pro Milone* (*Classical Review*, vol. xliii, No. 5). Throws light on the relation of Cicero to Lucretius.

HOGBEN, L., *Science for the Citizen*, Allen and Unwin, 1938.

JENSEN, C., *Ein neuer Brief Epikurs*, Berlin, 1933.

LACEY, P. H. DE, *The Epicurean Analysis of Language* (*American Journal of Philology*, Jan. 1939).

MARITAIN, J., *An Introduction to Philosophy*, Sheed and Ward.

MARTHA, C., *Le Poème de Lucrèce* (2nd ed.), 1873.

NILSSON, *A History of Greek Religion*, Oxford, 1925.

NIZAN, P., *Les Matérialistes de l'Antiquité*, 1936. Valuable for its understanding of the social implications of ancient materialism.

PATIN, *Études sur la Poésie Latine* (3rd ed.).

PLATT, H. E. P., *Byways in the Classics*.

REGENBOGEN, *Lukrez: Seine Gestalt in seinem Gedicht*, 1932.

REID, *Academica of Cicero*.

REINACH, S., *Orpheus* (Eng. tr.), Routledge, 1931.

ROBERTS, W. RHYS, *Dionysius of Halicarnassus*.

ROBERTSON, J. M., *A Short History of Free Thought* (3rd ed.).

SCHMIDT, W., *Epikurs Kritik der Platonischen Elementenlehre*, Leipzig, 1938.

SEIGNOBOS, *Essai d'une Histoire Comparée des Peuples de l'Europe*, Paris, 1938.

SIGERIST, *Introduction à la Médecine*.

SIKES, *Lucretius, Poet and Philosopher*, 1936.

SINKER, *Introduction to Lucretius*, 1937.

SOLMSEN, F., *The Background of Plato's Theology* (*Trans. of the American Philological Assoc.*, vol. lxvii, 1936).

TARN, *Alexander the Great and the Unity of Mankind*, 1933.
Alexander, Cynics and Stoics (*American Journal of Philology*, Jan. 1939).

TAYLOR, A. E., *Platonism*, Longmans, Green and Co., 1927.
Plato, The Man and His Work, Methuen, 1926.

THOMSON, G., *Aeschylus, Prometheus Bound*, 1932.

WALLACE, W., *Anaxagoras* (*Encycl. Brit.*, 9th ed.).

WHEWELL, *History of Inductive Sciences.*

WHITTAKER, *Priests, Philosophers and Prophets*, 1911.

WITT, N. DE, *Organization and Procedure in Epicurean Groups* (*Classical Philology*, July 1936).

WOODHOUSE, W. J., *Solon the Liberator*, O.U.P., 1938.

Index

GEORGE ALLEN & UNWIN LTD
LONDON: 40 MUSEUM STREET, W.C.1
LEIPZIG: (F. VOLCKMAR) HOSPITALSTR. 10
CAPE TOWN: 73 ST. GEORGE'S STREET
TORONTO: 91 WELLINGTON STREET, WEST
BOMBAY: 15 GRAHAM ROAD, BALLARD ESTATE
WELLINGTON, N.Z.: 8 KINGS CRESCENT, LOWER HUTT
SYDNEY, N.S.W.: AUSTRALIA HOUSE, WYNYARD SQUARE

Matter and Light

by Louis, Prince de Broglie

Demy 8vo.   *Translated by* W. H. Johnston   *About 12s. 6d.*

The results of modern physical research are probably the most vital product of the twentieth century. Recent investigations tending to demonstrate the affinity between light and matter appear to some observers to go to the very roots of an understanding of the physical universe. The present book is the vehicle of the views on this and kindred subjects of one of the most distinguished living workers in this field. The author's name vouches for their authority, while his nationality guarantees clearness and intelligibility.

Heredity and Politics

La. Cr. 8vo.   ## by J. B. S. Haldane   *7s. 6d.*

Are men born equal? Are there superior races? Should the unfit be sterilized? Is race-crossing harmful? Is the nation degenerating because the poor breed quicker than the rich? These are vital questions in the twentieth century. They are still being answered, both by would-be reformers and by conservatives, in terms of nineteenth-century science. Yet during this century we have learned more about heredity than in the whole preceding eternity. Some of these questions can be answered. Others turn out to be as meaningless as "Why does the sun go round the earth?" Others again cannot be answered until we know more.

Such are some of the topics dealt with in this highly provocative book by Professor Haldane, one of the most outstanding and challenging personalities in science and politics to-day.

Causality and Science

Cr. 8vo.   ## by Dr. Nalini Brahma   *6s.*

This book is at the same time an examination of the scientific concept of causality and a discussion of the metaphysics of the causal problem. It questions some of the fundamental assumptions of science and raises several important philosophical issues. In particular the Indian concept of causality is explained, examined and compared with corresponding Western views. The author endeavours to show the reconciliation between freedom and mechanism, spirit and nature, religion and science by explaining that determinism in the effect is quite consistent with indeterminism in the cause. The ever-puzzling doctrine of Māyā or the theory that the world is an illusion is here given in intelligible explanation.

The Quintessence of Bernard Shaw

La. Cr. 8vo. *by* Charles Duffin 7s. 6d.

The text of the first edition has been revised and largely rewritten to take cognizance of the plays that have appeared since 1920, and there are several new chapters specifically devoted to the recent work. (These new chapters have had the benefit of Mr. Shaw's personal emendation.) The book deals with Shaw as a great teacher, a thinker whose "Knobkerrying" is always followed by constructive proposals; and aims to elucidate the fundamentals of his gospel in such matters as Heresy, Sex, Politics and War, Economics, Education, and Religion. There is an examination of Shaw's creed of Creative Evolution, and of the attitude to Christianity taken up in *The Black Girl*, *Saint Joan*, and the Prefaces. The author believes the Shaw gospel to be in the main profoundly true, but does not hesitate to criticize it at a number of points.

The Original Bhagavad-Gita: The Song of the Supreme Exalted One

With Appendices and Analytical Notes by Rudolf Otto

Demy 8vo. *Translated by* J. E. Turner 10s. 6d.

In this translation of the Bhagavad-Gita Dr. Otto has distinguished what he regards as the original form of the ancient Hymn from later accretions. This extremely important and difficult analysis is accompanied by Critical Notes and Comments dealing with the many and varied aspects of a complex and subtle problem, and discussing the views already advanced by other leading authorities.

The Message of the Gita

as interpreted by Sri Aurobindo

Royal 8vo. *Edited by* Adilbaran Roy 10s. 6d.

The Gita may perhaps be called the greatest synthesis of Aryan spiritual culture, and Sri Aurobindo's famous book *Essays on the Gita* sets out its inner significances in a way that brings them home to the modern mind, and as the Calcutta Statesman says "carries to a new perfection the difficult task of expounding Hindu thought to the West." This commentary summarizes the substance of Sri Aurobindo's book and also contains the text of the Gita in Sanskrit, an English translation and lucid notes compiled verbatim from *Essays on the Gita*.

"The value of this book lies in the Notes which are the commentaries of the author. They interpret the text in a manner which is not obvious on the surface which serve to bring out the inner meaning of the Sanskrit."
—*The Times*

A Hundred Years of British Philosophy

by Dr. Rudolph Metz

Translated by Professor J.W. Harvey, Professor T. E. Jessop, *and* Mr. Henry Sturt. *Library of Philosophy*

Demy 8vo.   *Edited by* Professor J. H. Muirhead   25s.

Dr. Rudolf Metz's work is generally acknowledged to be by far the fullest and best history of recent British philosophy. The first part deals with movements which occupied the writers of the first fifty years of the nineteenth century; the second with the idealist movement which dominated the closing decades of it and with the pragmatist, and the older and newer realism which developed in the reaction against idealism. It ends with an account of the present state of natural philosophy, psychology, and the philosophy of religion. The author has written a Preface for the English edition and several new sections have been added to the German.

"The best history of recent British philosophy. . . . Dr. Rudolf Metz's monumental work has held this rank since it first appeared in 1935, and the present translation . . . is a worthy and necessary addition to a series of high repute. . . . Dr. Metz writes with an intimate knowledge of England, an unrivalled mastery of historical detail, and a considerable power of lucid exposition."—*Yorkshire Post*

Reality and Value

by A. C. Garnett

Demy 8vo.   Author of *Instinct and Personality*   12s. 6d.

"As an introduction to philosophical studies it will serve students admirably . . . it gives such a lucid and readable account of various theories which it is of consequence to know, that the student will find himself soundly instructed and wisely guided into the heart of philosophical discussion. . . . The style is simple and the argument is developed by easy stages, and altogether we can most cordially recommend the work."—*Expository Times*

An Essay on Critical Appreciation

by R. W. Church, M.A., D.PHIL.

Author of *A Study in the Philosophy of Malebranche, Hume's Theory of the Understanding*

Demy 8vo.   .   10s. 6d.

"A work of exceptional versatility and great philosophical power."—*The Times Literary Supplement*

"An interesting and valuable book."—*Time and Tide*

History of Science Library
Edited by Professor A. Wolf

A History of Science, Technology and Philosophy in the Eighteenth Century
by Professor A. Wolf

Royal 8vo.   *Illustrated*   25s.

"The rapid production of this work is exceedingly welcome to students, for there is no other comprehensive account in the English language of the parallel developments of science, technology, and philosophy since the Renaissance. The book contains a vast quantity of fascinating information. Professor Wolf's information excites a hundred questions for discussion. His treatise is one of the most important works of contemporary scholarship. It is essential for all students of modern history, who are both grateful for the work itself and for the speed with which it is being published."
—*Manchester Guardian*

Uniform with

A History of Science, Technology and Philosophy in the Sixteenth and Seventeenth Centuries

Royal 8vo.   *Illustrated*   25s.

Copernicus, the Founder of Modern Astronomy
by Angus Armitage, M.SC.

Demy 8vo.   *Illustrated*   10s.

"An able account of the life of the great astronomer and of his revolutionary conception of the Universe. Mr. Armitage's book will be useful to students of astronomy but the lucidity of his exposition should make it intelligible and profitable to the wider class of readers interested in the makers of modern thought."—*Scotsman*

"It is authoritative and will rank as a standard. Mr. Armitage is to be congratulated on having accomplished a fine piece of work and on having made a valuable addition to the library of scientific biography."—*Manchester Guardian*

The Chemical Studies of P. J. Macquer

Demy 8vo.   *by* L. J. M. Coleby, M.A., M.SC., PH.D.   6s.

"An interesting account of the life and work of the French chemist of the eighteenth century."—*The Times Literary Supplement*

(Complete list of the Library on application.)

All prices are net

LONDON: GEORGE ALLEN & UNWIN LTD